FINDING THE RIGHT CAREGIVER

GETTING THE BEST CARE

THE COMPLETE GUIDE TO GETTING GREAT IN-HOME CARE

JANICE WASHINGTON

Finding The Right Caregiver, Getting The Best Care

Cover and interior design by www.formatting4U.com

ISBN: 978-0-578-34199-6

Printed in the United States

This book is dedicated to the loving memory of my parents, John and Rosella, and to my wonderful and supportive husband, Arthur, who believed in this project and continually nudged me forward.

This book is also dedicated to the millions who struggle daily with dementia, to their families, and to the memory of Solomon Carter Fuller, M.D., an early researcher of Alzheimer's disease.

ACKNOWLEDGEMENTS

I am indebted to my friends, Toni and L.C., who encouraged me and made a path for me to follow. I also want to thank Amy Atwell for her guidance and Michele Wagner and Judi Fennell for their editorial assistance, support, and patience.

TABLE OF CONTENTS

CHAPTER 1

BEGIN WITH THE BASICS

If you've picked up this book, then you are at least open to the possibility that your parent needs more personal assistance than you, other family members, friends, and neighbors can provide. You may have a lot of questions, such as,

- what functions do caregivers perform?
- how much do they charge?
- how will you pay for their services?

Also, you may feel guilty for even considering hiring a caregiver, especially if your loved one or other family members are opposed to the idea. And even if you're positive your parent needs outside assistance, handling objections from other people can be challenging. If you have any of these concerns, don't feel discouraged. You are not alone. Without an emergency situation, such as a fall or sudden illness, it takes time for most people to commit to hiring a caregiver. What's important is that you are on the right track now, and this book can help you sort through these and many other issues.

How can I tell if my loved one needs outside help?

If you are concerned about your parent's behavior or physical state, you should first have them evaluated by a physician who specializes in geriatrics. Some symptoms are the result of treatable problems like dehydration or depression and are not necessarily an indication that your parent needs a caregiver. If their physician cannot find—or rules out—causes that can be cured or managed, the following behaviors and signs may indicate that your parent needs the services of a professional caregiver:

PHYSICAL OR PERSONAL MAINTENANCE DECLINE	MENTAL DECLINE OR EMOTIONAL CHANGES	INABILITY TO PERFORM HOUSEHOLD RESPONSIBILITIES AND MAINTAIN RESIDENCE
difficulty moving around or getting up from a chair	difficulty handling finances such as paying bills or balancing their checkbook; bills piling up; late notices or utilities turned off even though there is money available	failing to maintain their home and allowing the property to fall into disrepair; hoarding or refusing to get rid of broken items that cannot be repaired
falls	forgetting to take medication or failing to take medication as prescribed by their physician	failing to keep pets and their cages, litter boxes, etc. clean
not eating properly or an unexplained weight loss or increase in appetite	displaying a reluctance to leave home for fear of not getting back safely	burnt food or scorched cookware
a decline in driving skills resulting in accidents and tickets for driving infractions	failing to recognize familiar people	water left running in sink or bathtub
uncharacteristically unkempt appearance or an unpleasant body odor	a change in personality such as depression, anger, confusion, rapid mood swings, lack of interest in things and people, or a belief that people are stealing from them	
food or urine stains on the floor	seeing things or people that are not there; talking about "going home" or making plans to visit deceased relatives and friends	
	wandering off or trying to return to a previous residence or place of employment; being brought back home by a neighbor, a good Samaritan, or the police after becoming lost	
	becoming disoriented while driving home, ending up miles away, and not being able to explain how they got there or where they were going	
	wearing clothes that are inappropriate for the weather or wearing clothes inside out	

Family members often miss early signs that something is wrong. Initially, incidents occur so far apart that no one connects the dots. If it turns out that your parent needs assistance, do not minimize or dismiss your concerns. At the risk of being an alarmist, your parent's life could depend on securing in-home care for them—especially if your relative is prone to wandering or trusting strangers.

How can I figure out what caregiver services my loved one needs?

Some of your parent's care requirements will be obvious, especially if they are frail. Begin with a mental walk-through of their typical day. Start when your loved one wakes up in the morning. Can they get out of bed and walk to the bathroom unassisted? What about bathing and getting dressed? Now it's time for breakfast. Can your relative safely prepare a meal? You get the idea. Continue going through your parent's day and night activities until you have identified tasks where they could use help. To get the most complete picture, don't overlook activities that occur less frequently but are just as important, such as quarterly club meetings or regularly scheduled doctor visits. Can they get there and back safely?

Another useful technique is to document tasks that you or others currently perform for your parent. It is very easy to forget the things you do for them because you probably do not see helping as a big deal. However, if you were not available to assist your parent, someone else would have to step in.

Finally, compare your list to the two standard measurements that healthcare professionals use to determine the kind and level of assistance a person requires. The first is the term *Activities of Daily Living,* or ADLs, which refers to basic tasks that an individual needs to be able to perform for normal self-care. Additionally, a person needs to be able to perform more complex functions known as the *Instrumental Activities of Daily Living,* or IADLs, in order to live a completely independent life. Even if a person can perform ADLs, difficulty with IADLs may signal that the person needs a caregiver.

ACTIVITIES OF DAILY LIVING	INSTRUMENTAL ACTIVITIES OF DAILY LIVING
Eating	Housekeeping
Bathing and Oral Hygiene	Managing Finances
Dressing	Managing Medication
Grooming	Preparing Meals
Toileting	Shopping
Walking	Driving or Taking Transportation
Transferring and Positioning	Using the Telephone
	Taking Care of Pets
	Responding to Warnings or Alerts

ADLs:

Eating—Some people need to have their food cut up or fed to them. Also, caregivers can remind clients with dementia that they need to chew or swallow their food.

Bathing and Oral Hygiene—Caregivers help individuals bathe safely and reduce their likelihood of falling in the tub or shower. According to the National Institute on Aging, each year, over one-third of seniors at least sixty-five years old suffer a fall[i]. Many of these incidents occur in the bathroom. If your parent has to be bathed while lying in bed, make sure that you hire a caregiver who knows the proper technique.

Oral hygiene is often overlooked in the elderly and disabled population because more obvious health issues take priority, but gum disease can lead to serious problems, including heart attacks. Caregivers remind seniors to brush and floss daily and transport them to dental appointments. I found a dentist who made house calls and, through his mobile service, my mother continued to get check-ups on a regular basis. I wanted, at a minimum, to maintain the same oral health regimen she had before her stroke.

Dressing—Caregivers help people select and put on clothes, shoes, jewelry, and makeup. In the case of individuals with diminished mental capacity, caregivers may need to make the clothing selections rather than overwhelm their clients with too many choices.

Grooming—Personal care assistants comb, brush, and roll their clients' hair, as well as take them to the hairdresser and nail salon. Outings like these can work wonders for a person's self-esteem. This is especially true for people who have previously enjoyed these activities. Individuals who are no longer able to travel can have their hair washed at home by caregivers. Bedridden individuals can get a dry shampoo.

Caregivers also provide basic nail care to maintain clients' hands and feet. They should not work on more serious problems such as ingrown toenails, however. My mother's caregivers filed, shaped, and polished her fingernails. To ensure that her feet remained in good condition, I enlisted the services of a podiatrist who made house calls. More and more health professionals are offering mobile services to reach seniors who are homebound or for whom travel to a medical provider's office is problematic. I found both the mobile podiatrist and the mobile dentist through their respective professional association's local chapter.

Shaving is a key component of grooming for many men. A good shave helps a person look and feel better. A barber friend came to my parents' home to give my father a shave and a haircut after my father stopped leaving the house because of his dementia. I will never forget how his face lit up when the barber was finished and held a mirror up for my father to see himself. Keep in mind that many agencies will only authorize their caregivers to use electric razors.

Toileting—Toileting is probably the most sensitive area when it comes to caregiving. The simplest task is helping continent individuals position themselves on the commode, whereas the other end of the spectrum involves cleaning up after urinary or bowel incontinence. Incontinence can be extremely embarrassing—especially for a senior—and caregivers should do everything possible to maintain the person's dignity. What you want to look for in a caregiver is someone who is gentle, sensitive, and thorough in cleaning their client's private areas.

Help with toileting is also important because it gives caregivers an opportunity to monitor urine output and stool consistency. Changes in either can indicate illness, dehydration, or issues with diet or medication. Caregivers can then pass along any concerns to the client's family members or the client's physician.

Walking—Fall prevention is a common service that caregivers provide by: taking a senior's arm while walking to help steady the person; holding someone steady with a safety or gait belt; or handing an elderly person their cane or walker. Elderly people often resist using a cane or walker for fear that they will appear weak or frail. Caregivers can remind and encourage seniors of the benefits of using these assistive devices.

According to the Centers for Disease Control and Prevention, each year, three million seniors visit emergency rooms because of falls. Falls can result in bones that never heal, causing the senior to become an invalid for life. Sometimes infection or pneumonia sets in, leading to death.

Transferring and positioning—Caregivers help individuals safely transfer or move from the bed to a chair, wheelchair or commode, and back. Positioning also involves turning a bedridden individual on a regular basis so that pressure ulcers, also called bedsores, do not develop. The importance of knowing the right way to do a safe transfer cannot be overestimated. Failure to use proper procedures can put both clients and caregivers at risk of injury.

IADLs:

Housekeeping—Everyone can agree that individuals fare better in a clean and tidy environment. Caregivers perform light housekeeping duties such as washing the dishes and putting them away, emptying trash, sweeping, vacuuming, dusting, cleaning the bathroom, doing laundry, putting clothes away, and wiping countertops and stovetops. Making the bed and changing the linen on a regular basis also fall into this category. If caregivers have to change linen with your parent in the bed, be sure to mention this during the interview. There is a special technique for changing linen while someone is in the bed and, again, you want to hire experienced and proficient caregivers. This list of housekeeping duties is not exhaustive and is only meant to provide examples. However, caregivers are not expected to do heavy cleaning such as washing windows or anything that involves moving heavy furniture.

Managing finances—The ability to handle one's money (pay bills, budget, and keep track of income and expenses) is necessary to live independently. However, this is not an area where you necessarily want your parent's caregiver involved. Other options are discussed later in the book when a loved one cannot handle their financial affairs.

Managing medication—Cognitively impaired individuals can especially benefit from having a caregiver remind them to take their medication and inform whoever is coordinating their care when medication is running low and needs to be refilled.

Preparing meals—Planning and preparing meals are two of the most common duties performed by caregivers. Seniors know what they like and are fortunate if they find a caregiver who can prepare food to their taste. A high percentage of caregivers in the United States are foreign-born, and while they may be sensational cooks of their indigenous dishes, American cuisine is a challenge for many, at least initially.

I made a mistake early on by not being more specific about meal preparation when interviewing an applicant for a caregiver position for my mother. During the interview, I asked if she could cook. Being new to the process, I did not go into detail and simply accepted her answer that, yes, she could cook. Big mistake. Especially given that my mother was an excellent cook. I should have found out if the caregiver could prepare a few specific dishes that I knew my mother liked, and, if so, had the person describe how she would fix each one. If I had dug deeper, I would have discovered what mattered most—that the caregiver did not know how to cook American-style. My mother liked scrambled eggs, toast, grits, and prunes for breakfast. The first morning the caregiver fixed breakfast, she scrambled the eggs first and set them aside while she cooked the grits—and not the instant kind, either. My mother was not amused when the caregiver served her cold eggs. She scolded the aide over and over, saying, "eggs should be cooked last." I had to intervene and assure my mother that the caregiver had gotten the message. I had been in the back of the house making my mother's bed and straightening up, but I should have been in the kitchen to see what was going on since it was the caregiver's first day and her first time preparing a meal for my mother. After getting out the ingredients, skillet, and pots for the caregiver, I did not want to hover and make her feel nervous. I also *assumed* that the menu was pretty basic, but I should not have made any such assumption. The moral of the story is: take nothing for granted when selecting a caregiver. To my mother, the eggs were cold, but, to the caregiver, the eggs were room temperature and probably perfectly acceptable in her country of origin. The right way to do something, however, is the way the client wants it done—as long their preferences do not raise health or safety concerns.

Shopping—Caregivers take seniors shopping and help them make purchases.

Driving or taking transportation—By providing transportation, caregivers give seniors access to the larger community. Some clients prefer to use their own car because it is familiar and makes them feel more in charge.

Using the telephone—Using the telephone includes the ability to look up numbers, dial numbers, and answer the telephone. If needed, caregivers answer and place calls for clients and assist with basic technology.

Taking care of pets—Some caregivers are willing to feed, walk, or clean a pet's quarters, but it depends on the agency and the caregiver. Many care providers restrict their services to humans. Just as caregivers should not be expected to cook meals for the entire family, many do not feel they should have to tend to pets. Others are fearful of or allergic to certain animals. Be sure to disclose the presence of pets up front to avoid problems later.

Responding to warnings or alerts—Another key requirement for being able to live independently is having the ability to recognize and respond appropriately to warnings such as fire alarms. Individuals who can no longer recognize danger signals and get to safety on their own need the assistance of caregivers.

In addition to ADLs and IADLs, there are other areas—not formalized by the healthcare profession—where caregivers can play a significant role:

Companionship—Keeping a person company is the most basic type of caregiving and is usually provided for people who either cannot be alone all day or all night, or who simply feel more comfortable if someone else is in the home with them. Companions converse, play games, and watch TV with their clients. They also help individuals stay connected to friends and family through letters, Skype, Facebook, email, or texts.

Keeping seniors safe is another important aspect of companionship. The media have reported numerous instances where individuals with dementia wandered off, only to be found later injured or dead from exposure to extreme temperatures.

Facility Sitting—Hospitals are understaffed and nurses can take a long time to respond to call lights. Some people who are hospitalized for a short period (and who can afford it) pay a caregiver to sit with them for several hours a day during their stay. A private caregiver can alert the hospital staff when the person needs assistance and can keep the family advised about their relative's quality of care. For example, caregivers can verify if the staff is repositioning or turning the patient every two hours to avoid bedsores or if medication is being administered on time. They can make sure the person gets extra blankets if they become cold, and caregivers can turn back blankets if the person becomes too warm. These may seem small, but patients are particularly susceptible to pneumonia in hospital settings. I recall going to the hospital to visit my eighty-seven-year-old mother who slept under a comforter year-round (as do I) only to find her lying under one thin sheet with the air conditioner unit in her room going full blast. When I brought this to the staff's attention, the nurse said that my mother had seemed warm to the touch the previous night. The problem is, even if she was warm the night before, no one took the time to check on her periodically to see if her status had changed. A caregiver by my mother's side during the hours I was not there may have noticed that she needed more cover and prevented that and other instances of her needs not being met.

Paying caregivers to facility-sit has another benefit. Workers who continue to receive their pay are less likely to seek employment elsewhere. Like anyone else, caregivers have to earn a living. When clients are hospitalized, caregivers may be forced to move on to other jobs—especially when the client's discharge date is several weeks away or unknown.

In general, medical or skilled care is not required to assist someone with their ADLs and IADLs or to provide companionship. The services of a personal care or home care aide will suffice.

Licensed professionals such as registered nurses and physical and occupational therapists provide skilled care. Also, certified nursing assistants (CNAs) and home health aides can provide skilled care, such as changing dressings and taking vital signs, if working under the supervision of a licensed medical professional.

The job titles of caregiver, personal care aide, and home care aide are often used synonymously to describe non-skilled workers. Some people also include the term *home health aide*, while others make a distinction and limit this title to workers who provide skilled care. When discussing your parent's needs, make sure that the caregiver term being used means the same to everyone you are speaking with. Not only do you want to ensure that your loved one receives the appropriate type and level of care, but you do not want to pay for skilled care—which is more expensive—when the services of a home care aide will suffice.

If you're still unsure about the kind of care your parent needs, you can hire a geriatric care manager or you can contact your state Office on Aging for assistance. Many states have received Alzheimer's disease demonstration grants from the federal Administration on Aging to provide support to families in a variety of ways, including in-home assessments.

When you complete your list, your finished product will serve as the job description for your parent's caregiver. Next, figure out how many hours a day and how many days a week your parent needs assistance, and you will have made tremendous progress. Don't worry about getting the schedule perfect because you can always make adjustments by adding more hours or days or by decreasing coverage as needed.

Why pay for a caregiver?

In the United States, family members usually provide the bulk of caregiving services, but relatives are not always the answer. Paid caregivers can step in when family members live too far away to adequately care for a parent and relocation for either party is not an option for whatever reason. I once met someone who flew across the country three or four times a year to visit his divorced father who had dementia. His parent had trouble handling his finances, stayed indoors most of the time, and had few acquaintances. Nevertheless, his father felt that he was managing just fine and refused to move closer to his son. Parents often do not want to leave familiar surroundings or they may want to be close to a particular medical center or doctor. The son felt helpless and anxious with his father living alone so far away. This is a situation where the right caregiver would benefit everyone. The aide could provide companionship, try to interest the father in meaningful activities outside of the home, and serve as eyes and ears for the son.

Even adult children who live nearby are not necessarily in a position to assume caregiving responsibilities. They may have a job that requires long or irregular hours or that involves a lot of travel. Logistical issues, such as steps or the lack of a bedroom or bathroom on the first floor, can prevent a parent from moving in with their children.

Some people cannot act as caregivers for a parent because they have young active families which keep them on the go or they are already taking care of a family member and cannot assume the added responsibility of caring for someone else.

And let's be honest. Some people just don't have it in them—especially when personal care such as toileting and bathing is involved—no matter how much they love their parent. A person's unwillingness to help out is often construed as an indication that they do not *really* love their relative or else they would "do their duty," but some people simply cannot handle the responsibility that comes with caring for a parent. Moreover, each adult child's relationship with their parent is different from their siblings' and, therefore, the sense of obligation each feels toward their parent may vary—which is why guilt-inducing pronouncements of "but it's your parent" or "they took care of you when you were little" seldom change anyone's mind.

In other instances, the de facto family caregiver and the person needing help might have never gotten along or had a close relationship, in which case, it is best to seek assistance elsewhere. Adding the pressures of caregiving to an already strained relationship can create even bigger problems for all concerned.

Adult children who feel overwhelmed, anxious, resentful, guilty, overextended, frustrated, or sleep-deprived as a result of caring for a parent are not ideal caregivers either. They are more prone to give the wrong medication, have an accident, forget an important obligation, miss a deadline, or get sick because their immune system is compromised by stress and fatigue. It isn't that these relatives no longer *want* to take care of their parent, but they may have finally realized what others have been trying to tell them for years—that they *can't* keep this up. Some family caregivers haven't had a vacation in years and don't see how they can take one in the foreseeable future because their entire life revolves around their caregiving responsibilities. Furthermore, adult children who are still in the workforce may have to visit their parent's home before and after work and on weekends to take care of whatever chores need to be done. Then, they use the little bit of energy they have left for themselves and their own lives. This is a grueling schedule. If any of this sounds familiar, it may be time to hire a caregiver or, at least, give the idea serious consideration.

Also, many family members lack the necessary skills to care for a parent. I know that I was not equipped once my mother became bedridden. When I first tried to change her bed linen, it took well over an hour. My mother's professional caregivers could change her linen in less than ten minutes. My personal best never got below thirty minutes.

Finally, hiring a caregiver is often the only choice for many people who are single, divorced, widowed, or childless. It is estimated that as many as twenty-two percent of Americans over the age of sixty-five are or could become "elder orphans."[ii] This term describes older Americans living alone without the physical and emotional support of family and friends.

What do I do if my parent refuses to hire a caregiver?

It is very frustrating when a parent won't accept the fact that they need a caregiver. Family members may feel powerless to do anything about it, other than to wait for something bad to happen, which adds another layer of stress.

There are numerous reasons why people resist getting help. Your first step in this situation is to try to understand what the specific reason is behind your parent's refusal. They may not want a stranger in their house. If this is the case, listen thoughtfully to their concerns. News stories about dishonest and abusive caregivers can make anyone think twice. But, while caregiver abuse and neglect are valid concerns, statistics show that the perpetrator is most likely to be a family member. This is not meant to minimize the seriousness or likelihood of abuse at the hands of paid caregivers, but rather, to put the issue into perspective. You can also assuage your parent's fears by reassuring them that you are not turning them over to someone else and will continue to be very much involved in their care.

Your parent may also be concerned that a caregiver will take over the household or they may be uncomfortable or embarrassed at the thought of a non-family member being involved with such intimate functions as toileting.

Some seniors are reluctant to hire caregivers because of the expense. In 2021, the U.S. Bureau of Labor Statistics put the national average wage for home health and personal care aides at $14.07 per hour.[iii]

These concerns are all valid, but when an individual actually *needs* a caregiver, that must be the priority. Once you have established a clear need for a caregiver and are no longer wavering, you will find it easier to overcome objections. Here are some techniques you can use to try to convince your parent that hiring a caregiver is the right choice. Try to solicit support from someone else whose opinion they value or with whom they have always had a special relationship. Sometimes this is a grandchild. If this strategy works, be grateful and do not take offense that they said *no* to you but *yes* to someone else. Stay focused on the goal of keeping your parent well and safe.

Another approach is to ask your loved one if they feel they are doing a satisfactory job of caring for themselves. Be sure that your tone and choice of words do not imply that you think otherwise. Many seniors want help but fear that broaching the subject will result in their being placed in a facility. Once your parent knows they can receive care at home, they may become more receptive to hiring a caregiver.

Try asking your parent if they will accept a caregiver to assist with housekeeping chores only. As they become more comfortable with the idea of having an aide, they may feel more amenable to having someone help with personal care tasks as well.

See if your parent will agree to a two- or three-week trial period, after which they can terminate the arrangement if it isn't working. Your parent may be more receptive if they know that *they* will make the final decision and can opt out if they want. If you can find a caregiver who shares the same interests or hobbies as your parent, you may be able to work the person into the mix as a friend or companion. Your relative may find this arrangement more acceptable and less of a threat to their independence.

Another strategy is to introduce a caregiver in small increments. Maybe your parent will consent to a few hours a day, twice a week for starters. I remember going back and forth with my mother about hiring a caregiver after her first stroke. She was firmly set against the idea. It took a while, but I was finally able to convince my mother to hire someone just to keep her company on the weeknights. It was an easier pitch because a lot of seniors do not like being home alone at night. I asked a family friend of almost fifty years if she knew anyone interested in working as a companion and she recommended her sister-in-law.

Emma was perfect for the position. She was a retired federal government supervisor looking to supplement her retirement income. She did not have specialized caregiver training but she did have experience caring for her elderly mother who had several of the same health issues as mine. Emma was responsible, reliable, honest, friendly, and caring. My mother was older, but they were close enough in age to relate to one another. Even so, there was still an adjustment period as my mother got used to having someone else in her home. She sometimes felt the need to remind both Emma and me very emphatically that "this is my house." After a couple of months, things settled into a smooth routine and my mother began to accept the new arrangement. After about six months, she looked forward to Emma's arrival and even wanted her to come on weekends. But caregivers have lives too, and

Emma's weekends were taken up with grandchildren and church activities.

Once my mother became accustomed to having someone in her home, I was able to increase coverage with less opposition. I hired a second caregiver for weekends and a couple of weekdays. The second caregiver was much younger than my mother and was from Uganda. She and my mother never developed the same comfortable relationship my mother had with Emma, but the second caregiver was very reliable and respectful.

If none of these techniques work, then consider consulting a professional in the field. Geriatric care managers, also known as eldercare specialists and aging life care professionals, help resolve family conflicts because they are objective and can be honest without fear of damaging relationships. You can find geriatric care managers through the Aging Life Care Association (formerly National Association of Professional Geriatric Care Managers) (see Resources). Geriatric care consultants also often have booths at senior expos which are held across the country.

It is not unusual for past grievances, misinformation, and unhealthy family dynamics to prevent a family from reaching a satisfactory agreement regarding a parent's care. Mediation is another option for resolving disagreement—especially among siblings— regarding what is best for your loved one. Mediators do not take sides in a dispute; rather, they use their training to facilitate discussion among the participants and, hopefully, reach a resolution. Mediators usually charge a fee for their services. Some local courts and non-profit organizations offer the service for free or charge on a sliding scale based on income. Your state Office on Aging may be able to provide a referral.

Finally, asking for help for *yourself* may get your parent to accept outside assistance. If you are the primary caregiver and are worn out, you need to speak up. Let your parent know that if you do not get some help soon, your health will suffer and you will not be of use to anyone. They may not realize the toll that caring for them is taking on you. Or your parent may know and not care because their needs come first and always have. Regardless, reassure your loved one that hiring a caregiver does not mean that you are abandoning them. Stress how much you care about their welfare and that you want the best life possible for them. However, be clear about what you can and cannot do going forward. Suggest hiring a caregiver to perform the services that you can or will no longer provide. If your parent flat out refuses to have a caregiver in the home, you may have to accept that decision, in which case, cue the serenity prayer.

God, grant me the serenity to accept the things I cannot change,
Courage to change the things I can,
And wisdom to know the difference.

Other than that, there is little else you can do. Remember that your loved one is struggling to hold on to their independence, dignity, and the right to live life on their own terms.

It is understandable if you become frustrated and angry, but, if possible, avoid stressing yourself out because you have to stay strong and avoid burnout. And just because your parent does not feel comfortable hiring a caregiver today does not mean that they won't change their mind later. Your relative is doing the best they can one day at a time—just like you. Unfortunately, sometimes people only accept help when bad things, such as falls, happen. If this occurs, do not blame yourself because you cannot control everything and everybody.

The final care plan that I created included my mother's older sister (at her insistence), two paid caregivers, and me. We provided twenty-four-hour coverage for my mother and the arrangement lasted more than three years. My mother wanted to remain in her home and I honored her wish as long as I could. Then she had a second stroke which destroyed the limited mobility she had enjoyed and took away most of her ability to speak. My husband and I moved my mother in with us and, with a great deal of help from aides, cared for her until she passed.

To be honest, I may have made a different decision if my mother had been able to communicate after her second stroke.

However, because she could not, I wanted her close by so that I could monitor the care she received. She would not have been able to let me know if her caregivers were not doing what they were supposed to do or if they mistreated her in any way. It was the best decision I ever made and I never had any regrets. For one thing, without the experience and insight I gained caring for my mother, this book would not have happened.

CHAPTER 2

ISO THE IDEAL CAREGIVER

Bringing a professional caregiver on board can be a positive experience for everyone, but the process can be time-consuming and somewhat daunting. Once you hire the right aide, however, you will feel tremendous relief immediately. Most people who find a good caregiver will tell you that they were just lucky. Luck undoubtedly plays a part, but, in this chapter, you will learn how to turn the odds in your favor.

What qualities should I look for in a caregiver?

You want a caregiver who is qualified, experienced, reliable, trustworthy, respectful, good-natured, and compassionate. The caregiver should have good judgment and show initiative by bringing changes in your parent's condition to your attention and making useful recommendations without prompting. Your loved one should feel at ease and respected around the aide. One caregiver told me about a male client who seemed uncomfortable around her. He told his daughter that he was satisfied with the caregiver's services, which included help with bathing, but the caregiver could tell something was slightly off. One day she gently asked her client if he would prefer a male caregiver and he immediately answered, "Yes." The man expressed his appreciation to the worker for raising the issue. Her sensitivity and compassion made all the difference in the world to the client.

Also, look for a caregiver who will engage with your parent and not stay on their cellphone for most of the shift because "there is nothing to do." Taking an interest in your parent's favorite TV shows and watching them together is an easy way to create a shared experience. My mother's caregiver began bringing a domino set to work in the evenings to help pass the time and she taught my mother how to play the game. They had many laughs when my mother began winning most of the time even though she had just learned to play. Do not underestimate the importance of good interpersonal skills. Look for a caregiver for your parent, not a caretaker.

How do I find in-home caregiving services?

You can find help in one of six ways: (1) agencies, (2) word of mouth, (3) advertising by you or by the caregiver, (4) geriatric care consultants, (5) university students, and (6) prospecting. If you need more than one caregiver, you may have to use several avenues to find the right aides because there is a shortage of qualified workers due to strong demand and high turnover in the profession.

How do I find a reputable agency?

The best way to find a good caregiver agency is through referrals based on personal experience. But if you have to forge ahead on your own without a recommendation, the following questions will help you get the information you need to make an informed decision. I recommend interviewing two or three agencies before making a selection. Below are some pertinent questions to ask:

- Are they able to assign a caregiver who has experience with your parent's specific illness, condition, or needs? Some agencies offer a full range of caregiver services, while others specialize. Let the agency know if your parent needs a caregiver with a particular set of skills. For example, Alzheimer's is the most common form of dementia, but there are other types, such as Lewy body and vascular cognitive impairment, that have different symptoms.

The stage of your parent's illness or disease is also important when considering a caregiver. An aide may have work experience with individuals in the initial stages of dementia, but your parent may have advanced dementia where the behaviors are quite different. The lack of specialized experience is not necessarily a deal breaker, but at least you will know in advance that some on-the-job training is in order.

- Does the agency provide replacement caregivers if the caregiver scheduled to work is unavailable? Does the agency provide a way for you to contact the company at any time in case your caregiver does not show up, leaves early, or if you need to cancel their shift because of an unexpected trip to the hospital?
- How does the agency recruit its caregivers? I discovered that one agency I used had hired its workers immediately upon completion of their certified nursing assistant (CNA) program. The agency could pay them a lower rate because of their lack of experience. My mother ended up on the receiving end when the caregiver did not know how to change linen by herself while my mother was lying in bed. The worker told me that she was taught never to perform this task alone and always have another caregiver there to assist her. I guess that would be me. Her hours were from 10:00 p.m.-6:00 a.m. It never occurred to me to ask about the company's recruiting policy because I assumed that they only hired experienced caregivers—and many of them do. Another agency I used only hired caregivers after they had worked in a nursing home for at least six months.
- Is the agency licensed? Licensing requirements vary from state to state.
- How long has the agency been in business?
- Are their caregivers classified as employees or is the agency a referral service? If the company simply refers caregivers to clients, then the client becomes the employer. The implications of this arrangement are discussed in greater detail later in this chapter.

- How much does the agency charge? What is the threshold number of hours their caregivers have to work before overtime applies? Which holidays incur overtime rates? One of my mother's agencies charged overtime for Mother's Day. I guess the rationale is that caregivers sacrifice being with their family on this special day.
- Does the agency have a minimum number of hours their caregivers must work in order to accept you as a client? My agencies' minimums ranged from four to eight hours a day.
- How often has the agency raised its rates in the last three years and, if so, by how much?
- What is the payment process? Does the agency bill on a regular basis or does the agency expect you to automatically send in your payment?
- How much of your fee will go to the caregiver? You want to know if the caregiver's wage is competitive; otherwise, your caregiver may leave for a better paying job. I found as much as a five dollar per hour difference in pay among the agencies I used. Your caregivers will discuss among themselves what you pay them. So make sure that you are treating everyone fairly and that you have objective criteria for any wage differences. For example, the worker who bathed my mother and cooked her meals made more than the caregiver who provided companionship during the night shift.
- How does the agency perform background checks? Do they query national databases or just local records? Does the agency check the records of surrounding jurisdictions as well as previous places that the caregiver has lived? Does the agency have the FBI run a fingerprint check? You want to know whether the agency does a comprehensive screening or just a cursory check.
- Are their caregivers tested for drugs? If so, how often?
- Are their caregivers bonded and insured? Bonding covers theft and property damage and insurance covers job-related injuries.

- What type of training and certifications—such as CPR and first aid—do their caregivers have?
- Does the company provide ongoing training for its caregivers? When was the last training offered and what was the topic?
- On average, how long have their workers been with the agency, and specifically, how long has the caregiver who will be assigned to your relative been with the agency? This will let you know if the agency has had sufficient opportunity to observe and evaluate the prospective aide.
- Does the agency have a weight limit for clients, especially those who need to be lifted?
- If one of their caregivers is injured on the job, how will the agency handle it?
- What happens if one of their caregivers accidently injures your parent?
- If you are managing your parent's care long-distance, how can you verify that a caregiver arrived on time and completed their shift? Some agencies have their caregivers call in when they report for work and call again at the end of the shift. One agency I used required their workers to call in using our landline. The company wanted to be sure that the worker wasn't calling from their cellphone before they arrived at work.
- How much notice do you have to give to terminate service?

Check with your state about the status of an agency's license and with the Better Business Bureau for information about complaints against the agency. Also, investigate if the agency is Medicare-certified by checking sites such as www.alz.org and www.medicare.gov. The fact that a company is on the list is not the same as a recommendation; however, it does mean that the agency is supposed to adhere to certain standards. If a friend recommends an agency based on personal experience, ask if the company was receptive to client concerns and if the company moved quickly to resolve any issues that may have occurred.

Are there different types of agencies that provide home care?

Yes, there are different types of caregiver agencies. Some agencies provide medical or skilled care, some provide non-medical services, and other agencies provide both. Agencies that provide medically skilled and licensed staff are called skilled home health care agencies. The patient's plan of care is prescribed by a doctor and administered by healthcare professionals trained in areas such as wound care, pain management, tracheotomy care, catheter care, injections, and physical, speech, and occupational therapy. Medicare typically covers the cost of skilled care, but not on a long-term basis.

Agencies that provide non-medical care are called in-home care agencies. Their services include assistance with ADLs and IADLs and companionship. Medicare only covers the cost of non-medical care if the services are provided in conjunction with skilled care, but not as a standalone benefit.

In reality, despite the labeling distinctions, non-medical workers often provide skilled care under the supervision of trained medical personnel. This can happen, for instance, when a client develops a new condition such as a bedsore that needs medical treatment. A wound nurse may come to a client's home, examine the wound, develop a treatment plan, and train the caregiver on the proper technique for applying medication and changing the wound dressing.

Agencies also differ according to whether they employ their caregivers or merely serve as a referral service. Traditional agencies employ their caregivers. You pay the agency and the agency pays the workers' salary, payroll taxes, and other benefits. The agency also provides its employees with a W-2 (Wage and Tax Statement) for the tax year. This model provides the greatest liability protection for clients because their caregivers are bonded and insured. Even if an agency tells you that the company employs its caregivers, double check by asking if the agency withholds payroll and income taxes. You don't want to discover down the road that you are the caregiver's employer, in which case, *you* would be responsible for these tasks and many others.

A registry, referral, or staffing agency, on the other hand, is an employment service for workers. They do not employ their caregivers. Instead, clients pay the agency a one-time finder's fee or a contracted premium (around twenty percent) of the caregivers' earnings for the duration of the assignment. Some of these agencies perform background and reference checks just like traditional agencies. The client assumes the role of employer and pays the caregiver directly.

For decades, referral services treated caregivers as independent contractors to avoid paying minimum wage, overtime, and payroll taxes. But the federal government closed that door and, today, it is all but impossible to classify caregivers as independent contractors. However, if you are still not sure whether your worker is your employee or an independent contractor, you can submit Form SS-8 (Determination of Worker Status for Purposes of Federal Employment Taxes and Income Tax Withholding) to the IRS for a definitive answer. It may take several weeks for the government to get back to you.

What are the advantages of going through an agency?

Home care agencies have positioned themselves as the talent scouts of the industry. Those that employ caregivers take care of:

- recruitment
- hiring
- background checks
- employment authorization verification to work in the United States
- payroll
- insurance

- bonds
- replacement caregivers
- termination

Even if you go through an agency, however, you will still have responsibilities. You have to interview candidates the agency sends over and monitor and supervise their work. You can usually let the agency handle terminations, but there are some situations, such as abuse or neglect, where you must let a caregiver go on the spot.

As mentioned earlier, one of the advantages of agencies is they can probably find a replacement caregiver quicker than you can if your parent's aide suddenly quits, fails to show up, or does not work out. However, agencies struggle to find replacements too—especially at the last minute, which is usually when the need arises. Let's say that your caregiver calls fifteen minutes after they were due at work at 8:00 p.m. to say they won't be coming in. When you call your agency to request a replacement, the response is likely to be something along the lines of "We'll see what we can do," as opposed to, "We'll send someone over right away." It may take the company several hours, days, or even weeks to find someone with the right skillset who can work the required days and hours.

The more notice you give the agency, the more likely they will be able to find a substitute. But agencies have a difficult time finding replacement caregivers for night and weekend shifts and for clients with complex medical needs. Caregivers who worked the night shift for my mother failed to show up so often that I decided it was easier to assume the duties myself. I had to wait several hours for the substitute to show up. Then, I had to get up during the night to monitor the person and to see if they had any questions. I found that since I had to be up anyway, it did not make sense to pay someone for only a few hours of work.

One agency I used did not have a replacement caregiver for the weekend shift for over a month. Other times, the caregiver they sent could work on Saturday but not Sunday. Or the substitute could only work alternate weekends because they worked every other weekend at their full-time job. A lot of caregivers work in hospitals during the week and supplement their income with weekend caregiver jobs. All of this led to a revolving door of new caregivers, which meant more people for me to train and supervise. Other people I knew who were taking care of aging parents experienced the same problem. I finally gave up waiting for the agency to staff the weekend and night shifts and I hired workers directly. It is not unusual to cobble together caregivers from different sources to get the coverage your parent needs.

There is an acute shortage of caregivers in America as well as other countries with a significant aging population. Because of the high demand for services, agencies are springing up at a rapid rate and they are all vying for the same limited pool of workers.

I want to mention another claim agencies make that I did not find to be true—they supervise the caregivers they send to your home. The agencies I used provided no supervision whatsoever once the assignment began. The owner of one agency stopped by once after the caregiver began working to see how things were going. The other agencies simply told me to call them if I had any problems. The only time I heard from them was when a holiday was coming up. They wanted to know if I still needed caregivers because overtime rates apply.

What are the disadvantages of using home care agencies?

Agencies charge higher rates than what you would pay a caregiver you hire directly. In order to be profitable, agencies have to charge a premium to cover payroll taxes, insurance, overhead, advertising, paid leave, and training. These costs are passed on to clients in the form of higher rates.

Caregiver agencies are also more restrictive about the services they allow their caregivers to provide for clients. For example, many agencies only allow nurses to administer medication—read: higher hourly fee—and only allow their caregivers to remind clients to take their meds. If your parent needs assistance in this area, be sure to ask agencies about their policy. I pre-filled my mother's pill organizer each week and her caregivers handed her the pills.

If Medicaid funds your relative's long-term care, their state may require them to only use aides from a Medicaid-certified agency. Also, some long-term care insurance policies state that the company only pays for caregivers from agencies but not for caregivers you hire directly. If agencies consistently assign aides who do not work out, document everything and ask the insurance company to reconsider and make an exception. A friend of mine was successful in getting a major insurer to allow his mother to use private duty caregivers.

May I request a caregiver of a specific ethnicity or decline caregivers of certain ethnicities?

Some people have strong opinions about race and ethnicity, especially when it comes to personal care, and they do not suddenly become more open-minded when they become old, ill, or disabled. It is unusual—but not rare—for clients to specify a preference for a certain race or ethnicity or refuse to accept a caregiver for the same reason. Agencies will try to comply because they see no point in sending a worker to a client's home if the person will be turned away at the door or treated badly.

One problem with limiting one's choice of caregivers based on race or ethnicity is that many caregivers are immigrants. The client who refuses to accept a foreign-born caregiver may be waiting a long time for assistance.

Conversely, some agencies specialize in providing caregivers who know the language, culture, and cuisine of a particular ethnic group. This specialization is often found in agencies that serve Asian communities.

How can I find a good caregiver through word of mouth?

Word of mouth is the best way to find a good caregiver, especially if the person making the recommendation has firsthand knowledge regarding the aide's skills and work ethic. If you know a family who has a good caregiver, ask if their aide knows other good caregivers seeking employment. Caregivers look out for each other and they usually know who is looking for work.

Similarly, a family who had a great caregiver but no longer needs that person's services will be happy to put you in touch with their former aide. If their former caregiver is not available for work, ask the caregiver for other leads. This is the mindset you must have in order to find a good caregiver through word of mouth. At every opportunity—work, church, gym, dog park, social events—ask as many people as possible if they know of a good caregiver. Solicit names from book club members, alumni association happy hours, and charity walk-a-thons. Doctors and social workers can be good referral sources as well. In other words, work your everyday contacts to find your ideal person. Take the same approach that top salespeople employ to find new clients. They constantly network because they never know where their next sale might come from.

Don't be shy or reticent about letting people know you are looking for a caregiver. You would be surprised at how many people are in the same dilemma or know someone who is. They will understand and you never know who may be able to help you. Nowadays, more people are using caregivers and are only too willing to assist. I have helped find caregivers for people I don't even know because we had a mutual friend who put us in touch with one another.

Where and how do I advertise for a caregiver?

You can place ads in church bulletins, on Craigslist, in community newspapers, newspapers focused on senior issues, college newspapers, websites dedicated to caregiving issues—like care.com—and bulletin boards at community centers and grocery stores. Your ad should briefly but realistically describe the services your parent needs. Let applicants know what is expected and see if the job entails anything they do not know how to do or would not be comfortable doing. Avoid vague phrases such as "needs personal care services." Instead, state that your parent needs someone to cook, wash and put away the dishes, sweep, wash and iron clothes, clean the bathroom once a week or as needed, and dust the furniture once a week.

Highlight particular circumstances such as lifting required or that your relative is in the early stages of dementia. Also include the days and hours of the job, the start date, and contact information. At this point, it is not wise to include too much personal information such as your parent's address. Instead, reference a landmark or describe the general vicinity such as "near the University of Chicago" or "close to historic Annapolis." And let prospective applicants know they must provide references.

Caregivers also advertise their services in the same media outlets described above. Ads on care.com include the caregiver's age, experience, education, hourly rate, distance the person is willing to travel to the job site, languages, certifications, if the person has their own transportation, and a photo.

What role do consultants play in the search for a good caregiver?

Some families hire a geriatric care consultant to help find a good caregiver for their loved one. These professionals perform *needs assessments*, help determine a plan of care, identify community resources and services, work with agencies to find caregivers with the right skillset, mediate family disputes about care, and help families figure out how to pay for their loved one's care. Their services can be pricey. Some consultants charge by the hour —fifty to two hundred dollars—depending on the region of the country.[iv] Others charge a flat fee. Clients may also be responsible for out-of-pocket expenses incurred by the consultant, such as mileage and parking. If you decide to engage a geriatric care consultant, make sure you understand the fee arrangement and get the agreement in writing to avoid disputes in the future. A consultant should not recommend businesses in which they have a financial interest, but if the consultant does so, they should disclose the existence of any business or personal relationships.

Ask the consultant about their experience, education, and professional training, and ask for referrals. Find out if the consultant belongs to professional organizations such as the Aging Life Care Association (ALCA). Membership in the ALCA is voluntary, but the group has established Standards of Practice and a Code of Ethics. I recommend checking out the organization's website for more in-depth information on ways in which these professionals can help families coping with long-term care issues (see Resources).

Many services that geriatric care consultants provide are quite valuable, but I do not recommend paying a consultant just to find a caregiver unless you are managing your relative's care long-distance, family members cannot agree on how to proceed, or the task seems too daunting and you would just rather hire someone to handle the search process. I contacted a geriatric specialist when asking people for recommendations did not produce any leads initially. My mother was still living in her home at the time. The consultant asked what kind of assistance my mother needed, about my mother's likes and dislikes, and what qualities we were looking for in a caregiver. She said that she only used two agencies because, in her experience, their caregivers were always very good. I answered the consultant's questions and told her that my mother needed someone to work from 8 a.m.–5 p.m. during the week. The consultant contacted me a couple of days later to say that she had arranged an interview with a candidate and invited me to attend. Based on the applicant's resumé, she was qualified. However, during the interview she casually mentioned that she was in the process of seeking custody of her two elementary school-age grandchildren and would need to take time off to attend court hearings. I wasn't unsympathetic, but my mother's need for a reliable caregiver was my priority. Also, not too long into the interview, it became obvious that the consultant had never met or even spoken with the candidate prior to our meeting. Instead, she had relied on her contact person at the caregiver's agency to select someone appropriate. After the meeting, the consultant apologized, made a poor excuse about how this candidate was not representative of the quality of aides she usually recommends, and offered to waive her fee for the time she had spent so far. It was at that point that I realized *I* could have contacted an agency myself, described the services I needed, and interviewed potential candidates on my own. For one hundred dollars per hour, I thought that the consultant would, at least, have spoken with the caregiver beforehand. Because taking care of my mother was so new to me, I bought into the exclusivity of the agencies that she dangled before me and I saw the consultant as a lifeline. I thought that she had the inside track on finding the best caregivers.

The next applicant the consultant arranged for me to meet seemed great at the outset. As the interview progressed, however, it became apparent that the consultant had never spoken with this caregiver either and that this applicant would not work out. She was a live-in caregiver for another client and her tour of duty was the night shift. I expressed concern about how she would be able to care for my mother during the day after working the night before. She explained that the live-in position was mostly providing companionship in the evening and that she slept during the night. Her shift ended at 7:00 a.m. and then another caregiver relieved her. Upon hearing this pertinent information that *I* elicited—*not* the geriatric care professional—I immediately identified two problems. First, I needed someone who could relieve my mother's night caregiver by 8:00 a.m. However, this applicant would have to travel over twenty miles in morning rush hour traffic in the Washington, D.C. metropolitan area to get to work. The nation's capital consistently rates as having one of the worst commutes in the country. I also asked what would happen if her relief caregiver was late or did not show up at all. The interviewee was candid about the fact that the other client had priority because that job also provided room and board. She acknowledged that she would not be able to leave her client until the other caregiver arrived. I totally understood and thanked the applicant for being so candid. As we walked out together, she apologized because things did not work out. She explained that her agency does not allow the caregivers to speak to the client beforehand for fear the two parties would reach an agreement and cut the agency out. I understand the company's policy, but the result is that both of us had wasted our time. If the agency had just told the caregiver where my mother lived, this would have been enough information for her to figure out that the work schedule was not feasible. More to the point, my high-priced consultant could have discovered all of this ahead of time and saved us all a lot of trouble. I terminated my contract with her after realizing that she did not hold the keys to the kingdom. So, unless you need a geriatric care consultant for other services, I recommend contacting agencies directly to find a caregiver. The agencies will send candidates for you to interview and you are not under any obligation to hire someone just because the agency sent them.

Are students a good source for caregiver services?

I like the idea of using student help because they have down time between classes and their weekends are usually free. Many of them make ideal companions for individuals needing minimal or intermittent assistance. Students can do the grocery shopping, cut grass, shovel snow, and perform light housekeeping tasks. They could be paid outright, reside in your parent's home in exchange for services, or be compensated by a combination of the two. Having someone stay in an elder's home at night also provides additional security.

You may want to consider students in graduate school because they tend to be older, more mature, and less into the school's social life. One downside of using student help was exposed when the coronavirus pandemic hit. Countless colleges and universities were forced to cancel in-person classes for the safety of their students, faculty, and staff and, instead, held classes online. As a result, many students who worked as caregivers for the elderly and disabled did not return to campus, leaving many individuals stranded.

If you would like to explore this possibility, contact the career services office of colleges and universities in your area. Just remember that students graduate and usually move on, meaning you will have to start the cycle all over again at various intervals.

How do I "prospect" for a good caregiver?

Finally, a little-known way to find a good caregiver is a technique I call "prospecting." Prospecting is nothing more than keeping your eyes and ears open for all possible leads, especially when you are in a medical setting such as a rehabilitation center or physician's office where individuals are often accompanied by their caregiver. My uncle found my grandmother's aide this way. Her children had been trying to find a good caregiver for months with no success. Then, unfortunately, my uncle had a stroke and his physician sent him to rehab. During one of his therapy sessions, he noticed another patient arriving for her appointment accompanied by her caregiver. There was something about the way the caregiver interacted with her client that caught my uncle's attention. At the end of his session, he made his way over to her and asked if she was available to take on other work. As it turned out, her client only had a few more therapy sessions left, after which the caregiver would be able to take on a new assignment. A few weeks later, our family hired the caregiver my uncle met at rehab and she stayed with my grandmother until she passed six years later.

Many nurses and nurse's aides take on private duty work on their off days. If your loved one is hospitalized and you notice a particularly efficient and attentive employee, ask if the person would be interested in part-time work. Of course, this should be a private conversation and not held in front of other hospital personnel.

What are the advantages of hiring a caregiver on my own?

There are three main benefits to hiring a caregiver directly, with the biggest advantage being cost savings. I found the cost of a private duty caregiver to be between twenty to fifty percent less than what agencies charged. Second, a direct hire is also more likely to perform duties that many agencies would not allow, such as administering medication or handling tube feedings. In my experience, however, many caregivers from agencies are eager to acquire new skills and I trained most of them how to do tube feedings. Third, hiring on your own means you are not limited to the workers who are on a company's roster. If you hear about or meet someone great, you are free to hire that person.

What are the cons of hiring caregivers on my own?

The biggest challenge about being the employer is finding substitute caregivers—especially on short notice. You will need a backup plan when—not *if*— your regular caregiver misses work. And the more vulnerable your parent is, the greater the need to find replacements quickly. Life happens to caregivers, too, and you have to be sensitive to that fact. They get sick. Their cars break down. Caregivers have childcare and relationship issues, just like everyone else.

There are ways to address this problem, short of using agencies exclusively. If you utilize more than one caregiver, they may be able to pinch-hit for each other. The caregivers I hired were great about stepping in when one of them had to skip work. Another option is to use agency caregivers for backup only in the interim. That way, as soon as your regular caregiver returns or you hire someone new, you can terminate the contract with the agency. As you can see, nothing about caregiving is an either/or proposition. Flexibility and ingenuity are your guiding principles.

Also, hiring private caregivers is time-consuming and demanding. As the employer, you are responsible for doing everything agencies do—recruiting, interviewing, hiring, scheduling, training, and paying caregivers. You must contact references, do background checks, and terminate caregivers, if necessary. In addition to paying workers, handling payroll consists of (1) withholding and remitting your employees' income taxes, (2) withholding and remitting the employee's payroll taxes (Social Security and Medicare), (3) paying your matching share of payroll taxes, (4) paying unemployment insurance at both the federal and state level, where required, (5) paying insurance, and (6) paying workers' compensation. Each year, you must provide all caregivers with a W-2 by the deadline set by the IRS and maintain detailed records in accordance with federal and state law. IRS Publication 926 entitled, "Household Employer's Tax Guide and the Instructions for Schedule H," is an excellent source of information on employers' legal obligations. A few states require employers to provide disability insurance, which replaces a percentage of a worker's income when the employee cannot work due to a non-work-related injury. Contact your state employment office for more information.

Frankly, I found the paperwork associated with payroll overwhelming and time-consuming because I also provided a lot of hands-on care for my mother. I was the point person for everything. To take some of the load off, I used Paychex, a payroll services company. All I had to do was call the company weekly with the number of hours each caregiver had worked. Paychex then made direct deposits to the workers' bank accounts, prepared and mailed W-2s to them at the end of the tax year, and prepared all required state and federal tax filings for my mother's tax returns. Using a payroll service was one of the best gifts I gave myself during this challenging time and it was a lifesaver in my case. I no longer had to spend time doing paperwork or rush to meet filing deadlines. I chose Paychex, but there are numerous companies to choose from. Also, payroll services companies are not the only option. For a fee, some agencies that serve as a caregiver-referral service offer clients the option of having the agency take over these tasks.

Under this arrangement, families hire caregivers directly but leave the paperwork to the agency. A word of caution is in order, however. Even if an employer hires another party to perform the payroll function, the employer is still responsible for seeing that it is carried out in an accurate and timely manner. In other words, employers cannot outsource their obligation.

If you like the idea of someone else handling payroll, your caregivers will need to have a bank account for direct deposit. Some caregivers are "unbanked," meaning that they do not have a checking or savings account. Others have a bank account but operate primarily outside of the banking system and use money orders, check cashing services, and payday loans. These individuals are referred to as "underbanked." A caregiver I employed was unbanked and asked to have her wages put on a prepaid debit card. She used the card to pay for everything, including her rent. She even received her income tax refund on her card. I agreed to put her weekly pay on her card only once. I did not like disclosing my Social Security and driver's license numbers to the store clerk and found the entire process to be a hassle in general. I told the aide that, going forward, I would pay her by check and she would be responsible for cashing it. Whatever payment method you select should include clear proof of payment. I know that cancelled checks qualify.

What questions should I ask when I interview potential caregivers?

The key to developing effective interview questions and, ultimately, having a good interview, is preparation. The duties you need a caregiver to perform for your parent will form the talking points for your meeting. You want to ask open-ended questions, which elicit more information than simple, "Yes" or "No" responses. You want the candidate to tell you as much about themself as possible. If feasible, have your parent participate in the interview.

- Tell me about your previous experience as a caregiver.
- How did you become interested in this profession? Many workers are attracted to caregiving because of the low barriers to entry, which range from no training requirements at all in some states to a few weeks of study in other states. A lot of caregivers will say that they "like helping people," or they planned to become a nurse but things didn't work out and their plans got derailed along the way. One of the best answers I got to this question was from the caregiver who took care of my grandmother and then my mother. She said that when her brother became seriously ill, she volunteered to take care of him. Through this experience, she discovered that she was really good at taking care of others. After learning people were willing to pay for the kind of services she had provided for her brother, she decided to make her living in the field. I thought her answer rang true because few people grow up wanting to bathe, feed, and clean strangers.
- Do you have experience with [the specific duties in the job description you created]? If applicants tell you they have experience bathing bedridden clients, find out how long they have performed this task and under what circumstances. If they perfected their skill in a nursing home or hospital, they probably have a decent technique. If they only bathed someone as part of their practicum for their CNA certification, then they are not experienced.
- Have you ever worked with a client who has [fill in the illness or condition] and if so, what was your experience like?
- Inform prospective caregivers about specialized medical equipment they will have to operate such as a suction machine or Hoyer lift, and ask if they have experience using the equipment.
- Do you have any specialized training or certifications? If so, ask the caregiver to provide written proof.

- How would you handle a client who becomes angry, confused, or agitated? Give candidates hypotheticals, such as a client with dementia who wants to leave home to visit a long-deceased relative, withdraw all of their money from the bank, or accuses the caregiver of stealing, and ask how they would handle these situations.
- How will the caregiver spend time with your loved one other than watching TV? This question gets at if and how the caregiver would provide mental stimulation for your parent.
- Please provide examples of suggestions you made on previous jobs that resulted in better care for your client.
- What were some things you liked about previous jobs, as well as things you did not like and why?
- What do you find most challenging about being a caregiver?
- If the position calls for cooking, ask what dishes the caregiver is good at preparing. Once you hire a caregiver, if possible, show the caregiver how to fix your parent's favorite foods. Be sure to mention any dietary restrictions or food allergies.

During the interview, notice how a prospective employee is dressed. Is the person's clothing clean, neat, and pressed? You can tell when people take pride in their appearance and spend a few extra minutes to pull their outfit together. Did the caregiver arrive at the interview on time? Did they introduce themself to your parent? Did the applicant ask questions that demonstrated an understanding of the position? Does the caregiver seem physically capable of performing the responsibilities of the position?

Is there a difference in the quality of care provided by agencies and privately hired caregivers?

When it comes to non-medical care, there is no difference. There are good and bad caregivers among agencies and within the same agency, and there are good and bad private duty caregivers. Many of the same caregivers who work for agencies take on private duty work when the agency does not have an assignment for them. Some aides even prefer private duty work because they can make more money.

Do certified nursing assistants provide better care?

I used both licensed and unlicensed caregivers and did not find that one group provided better care than the other. CNAs *should* have a leg up when it comes to changing a bedridden person's linen but, as I discussed earlier, there is no guarantee. One CNA did not know how to operate my mother's oxygen tank but another worker did. Another CNA failed to call 911 when my mother had a stroke. Instead, she wasted valuable time calling my mother's sister and waiting for her to arrive. I saw CNAs use improper techniques. It just depends on the caregiver. Some people are quick learners and have an aptitude for this kind of work.

One benefit of hiring licensed caregivers is you can check your state's CNA database for disciplinary actions, whereas most states have no system in place to track abuse, neglect, or fraud committed by unlicensed personal care aides.

Do my parent and their caregiver need to have a written contract?

If you hire a caregiver, even a family member, you should formalize the arrangement with a written contract, also known as a personal care or support services agreement. I recommend hiring a lawyer to ensure that the document meets all state requirements. For example, some states require these contracts to be notarized.

Paying family members to provide care is relatively new, but the practice is gaining acceptance. A written contract has many advantages, such as transparency for the benefit of other family members. Siblings can be assured that money going to the family caregiver is for services rendered and not because of undue influence, favoritism or financial exploitation. The caregiver may have given up a paying job with benefits to care for the elderly person and being compensated mitigates their loss of income. The rate of pay should be comparable for the locale and not disproportionately high.

Also, your parent may need to apply for Medicaid in the future. The government will review all transfers of assets that your parent made during a certain time frame—known as the "look-back period"—to determine if the transfers were made to reduce assets for the purpose of qualifying for Medicaid. Without a written contract for services, it may be difficult to prove that prior payments were not gifts. For most states and the District of Columbia, the look-back period is five years preceding the date of the person's Medicaid application. If violations of this rule are found, the state will impose a penalty period during which your parent is ineligible to receive Medicaid assistance. The period of ineligibility is based on the amount of transfers and the average cost of nursing home care in that jurisdiction.

There are ways to transfer assets without delaying Medicaid benefits. A lawyer with Medicaid planning expertise can help you avoid committing unintended violations.

What terms should a caregiver contract include?

Below is a list of terms that any caregiver agreement should cover at a minimum:

- names of the caregiver and the employer—which may be your parent, you, or someone else
- date the contract commences and date the contract ends, if known
- detailed description of services (e.g., bathe daily, change linen once a week or as needed, prepare breakfast and lunch, sweep, vacuum, and mop client's room weekly, and maintain daily log of services performed and medications admin-

istered). Be as detailed as possible and avoid vague phrases such as "help with housekeeping." If the caregiver finds out later that the actual responsibilities are more involved than what they were led to believe, then they may want to renegotiate the rate of pay or they may leave.

- location where services will be provided
- work schedule
- name of person receiving the care
- rate of pay
- pay schedule
- number and length of breaks
- sleep period (for live-ins)
- benefits, if applicable
- mileage reimbursement rate
- termination clause (e.g., at will, upon two weeks' notice)
- signature of caregiver and client or client's representative
- date the contract is executed

You may be able to pay an agency on a monthly basis, but a lot of privately hired caregivers want to be paid weekly. Allow for revisions to the work schedule by the employer and by the employee with the employer's approval. The employer should be able to terminate the agreement at will. Two weeks' notice is customary for termination of an employment contract by an employee. All changes should be memorialized in writing.

Also, be sure to carefully read agency contracts. If the agency claims to perform background checks on their workers, then their contract should state this. A Michigan family sued their parents' home care agency for failing to do a thorough background check on the caregiver the agency provided after discovering the caregiver had stolen between $500,000 and $1.5 million from their parents. At the time she was placed in the home, the caregiver had two misdemeanor convictions as well as two outstanding felony warrants. The trial judge dismissed the claims on the grounds that the contract did not specifically state a background check would be performed even though the company had verbally told the family they did background checks on their workers.[v] It is not known if the family appealed the court's decision.

Is hiring a caregiver who is a senior themselves a good idea?

Elders in good health can make excellent caregivers. It is a good way to supplement retirement income and help others. With ties to the community and previous work experience, senior caregivers have a wealth of knowledge. They are also likely to be more reliable, patient, and empathetic. Some seniors offer their services as a companion and driver only because providing personal care is too strenuous.

What is a live-in caregiver?

A live-in is a caregiver who lives at the client's home permanently and has no separate residence of her own *or* who resides on the client's premises for an extended period of time but maintains a separate residence. According to the U.S. Department of Labor, an extended period of time means that the caregiver spends at least five days a week (one hundred twenty hours) at the client's home *or* spends less than one hundred twenty hours at the client's home but resides there five consecutive days or nights.[vi] If your parent requires twenty-four-hour care or close to it, you may want to consider a live-in arrangement.

With live-in caregivers, scheduling options depend on your parent's needs. Some people are more comfortable having someone in the home at night "just in case" but they do not routinely require assistance during this period. In this instance, a live-in just for the night shift might work. If needed, your parent could still employ other caregivers during the day who are not live-ins. Live-in caregivers are not available to work all day every day.

Be wary of someone who offers caregiver services in exchange for a place to stay. It might make good economic sense for a caregiver to give up an apartment they only stay in two nights a week and move in with your parent, but there are other considerations. Will the caregiver expect to host their friends and family at your parent's residence? A written contract with an exit clause can prevent a messy situation later if things do not work out and it becomes necessary to terminate the agreement. You want to avoid a situation where evicting the caregiver is your only recourse. Consulting an attorney about the relevant laws in your state and the best way to protect your loved one is money well spent.

My parent resides in an apartment. Will the live-in caregiver have to be added to their lease?

It depends. Ask the landlord if they would be willing to add an addendum to your parent's lease authorizing the caregiver to occupy the premises but not require the caregiver to become a tenant. Also, many leases require tenants to let the landlord know when someone else moves in and specify how many people may live in the unit. If your parent's lease has such a provision, make sure that they comply. Otherwise, the landlord may determine that your relative violated the terms of the lease and could ask them to move out.

If your parent meets the legal definition for being disabled, under fair housing laws they might be entitled to a reasonable accommodation such as a live-in caregiver. Under these circumstances, the landlord should allow the caregiver to reside in the apartment as an occupant instead of a tenant. But do your homework and don't assume anything.

Should I do a background check on the caregivers I hire?

The National Employment Law Project conservatively estimates that as many as seventy million adults in the United States have arrest or conviction records.[vii] According to a different national study, applicants for long-term care jobs are three times more likely to have a criminal record than the general population.[viii] Therefore, if you hire a caregiver you have not known personally for many years, it is essential that you run a background check on that person. You do not want anyone with a history of violence, theft, substance abuse, or other troubling behavior to have access to your parent or their property.

"Background check" is a general term that encompasses many different databases such as:

- criminal and civil court records
- professional licenses and certifications
- references and employment history
- sex offender registries
- driving record
- authorization to work in the United States

These days, you should also Google applicants. You may find social media content that eliminates applicants from further consideration. A word of warning: don't believe everything on the internet. According to one site I came across that claims to provide personal information about people, my husband of more than two decades is single and I have a criminal history. Of course, no specifics were given regarding my legal transgressions.

Performing background checks is tedious and cumbersome because information is stored in so many different places. Also, laws are constantly changing about who can access data about job applicants.

The easiest way to do a background check is to hire a company to perform this service. The cost will depend on how in-depth or comprehensive an investigation you want. Also, in some states, you may need written authorization from the applicant to access certain information.

How can I do my own investigation to see if a caregiver has a criminal background?

A criminal background check searches county, state, or federal criminal history files. This information primarily comes from court records. Some jurisdictions provide online access to court records. You can also visit the courthouses where files are maintained to see if an applicant has a criminal history. Some state laws restrict the type of information that employers may request and use by:

- not revealing criminal records that are older than a specified number of years if requested for a background check
- prohibiting employers from inquiring about arrest records that did not result in a conviction
- prohibiting employers from requesting criminal records until they have deemed the applicant "otherwise qualified" or are ready to make a job offer

Alternatively, you may ask an applicant to obtain a criminal background report from state and local law enforcement. For an additional charge, states will submit the person's prints to the FBI to check against the national database or the person can contact the FBI directly. The FBI will produce an Identity History Summary or "rap sheet" based on fingerprints in its database or will provide proof that no summary exists. Results can take a few weeks due to demand. If you decide to hire the candidate, consider reimbursing the person for the cost of the background check.

My sister-in-law worked for the local police department and she needed a caregiver for her mother during the day. During one interview, she asked a prospective employee if there was anything in her background that my sister-in-law should know before she ran a criminal background check. The caregiver then admitted that she had an arrest record for assaulting her grandmother. Up until that point, my sister-in-law had planned to offer the caregiver the job because she seemed perfect for the position.

If the caregiver's name is not found in the criminal records database, does this mean they do not have a criminal record?

A criminal records search has several drawbacks. Jurisdictions vary as to what information they will release to employers. Information can be inaccurate, incomplete, and out of date. Many states allow people found guilty of a misdemeanor to have their record sealed if they have not gotten into any more trouble after a specified period. Some people can get their record expunged if, for example, they complete a court diversion program.

Should I check civil court records?

Civil court records can provide valuable insight into whether an applicant has a history of dishonesty or if the person is litigious. A search would also let you know if a restraining order was ever taken out against the person.

How do I check a candidate's employment history?

Applicants should provide you with a copy of their resumé listing previous employers. By contacting the caregiver's past employers, you will be able to confirm what the person has already told you about their experience and length of tenure at each job. You can also find out if there are any unexplained gaps in the applicant's work history.

A prospective caregiver claims to be a CNA. How can I check the person's credentials?

Individuals who complete a prescribed course of study and pass a CNA exam may apply for state certification. Each jurisdiction maintains a registry of nursing assistants, who have been certified by the state. Not all caregivers are CNAs, in which case, the state probably will not have any information about them. Every state has its own criteria and procedures for access to the registry. A signed or sometimes notarized release form from the caregiver is required by some states before the licensing board will respond to an inquiry, but many states make the information available online to the public. Illinois provides a physical description, including height and eye color, to ensure that a caregiver is not using someone else's credentials. Arizona maintains a database of imposters who claimed to be certified by the state. To query your state's CNA registry, you will need the caregiver's first and last names, and, in some instances, their date of birth, Social Security number, or CNA certificate number. Some jurisdictions will only release information to the CNA or to health care providers such as nursing homes and caregiver agencies. In this latter instance, the CNA will have to request the information on your behalf.

What are good questions to ask when checking a candidate's references?

The purpose of conducting a reference check is to verify key information the applicant has provided, as well as to get a sense of the person's qualifications, reliability, and overall potential. Below are several questions to ask a reference:

- When did [applicant's name] work for you?
- What were their job duties?
- Were they a reliable worker and did they come to work on time?
- What were their strengths and weaknesses as a caregiver?
- If they were part of a team, how did they work with the other caregivers?
- Can you think of any difficult or stressful situations that they had to handle and how would you assess their performance?

- Would you hire [applicant's name] again if the opportunity presented itself?
- Can you think of anything else that might be helpful for me to know in making a decision about hiring [applicant's name]?

Are there elder abuse registries that I can check?

All states maintain registries of disciplinary actions taken against licensed CNAs. Generally, the state board of nursing is responsible for maintaining and updating these records. Some licensing boards (Oregon, Maine) give detailed facts about violations while others (New Mexico, Ohio) release only cursory information. Delaware has an online Adult Abuse Registry that includes *anyone* with a civil finding of abuse, neglect, mistreatment and/or financial exploitation, not just CNAs.

According to a 2018 report by the National Adult Protective Services Association, over half of the states maintain an APS abuse registry.[ix] Unlike state nursing board registries, the APS registries include unlicensed individuals. These databases are invaluable because they provide another means for screening out caregivers with a history of abuse. However, most states restrict access to certain kinds of employers, such as agencies, and, unfortunately, do not make their registry available to the general public. There are a handful of states that do, and it is worth checking to see what your state's policy is.

The federal government also maintains a List of Excluded Individuals/Entities prohibited from working in health facilities and programs that receive federal funding such as Medicare and Medicaid (see Resources). There are several reasons an individual could be on the list, including abuse, neglect, fraud, and drug violations. This database is useful because if someone is on the list, do you really want them working in your parent's home? Just be aware that caregivers can apply for reinstatement. Also, the names in the database are under the name violators were using when they were placed on the list.

If the state CNA registry does not show disciplinary actions against a caregiver, can I be sure that no abuse claim was ever alleged or substantiated against the person?

These databases can be extremely useful, but the information does not always present a complete picture for the following reasons:

- Many states allow CNAs to petition to have findings of abuse removed after a specified period of time (sometimes as little as six months) or after submitting proof of rehabilitation (Minnesota). This means that, depending on when you run your check, the name of an abusive caregiver may no longer be in the registry.
- Some states update their records sporadically.
- A few jurisdictions delay entering a finding of abuse until the CNA has exhausted their appeal rights.
- Some state registries only contain names of CNAs found to have abused a vulnerable adult after the abuse registry was established by state law, even though the states have information about offenses that pre-date the registry. If your state did not establish an elder abuse registry until January 1, 2010, for example, then CNAs who abused vulnerable adults before that date may not appear in the registry.
- Most state registries only contain the names of licensed CNAs who abused patients in a Medicare or Medicaid-certified facility such as a nursing home but not unlicensed individuals working in private residences.

How can I check to see if a caregiver applicant is a registered sex offender?

All states maintain a sex offender registry. The registries vary by which offenses are included, how long offenders remain in the database, and how much of this information is made available to the public. In 2005, the U.S. Department of Justice established the National Sex Offender Public Website which connects sex offender databases from all fifty states, the District of Columbia, tribal governments, and territories (see Resources).

Checking these registries is fairly straightforward and you can query by name. Because the databases are maintained by each state, the frequency with which they are updated is not uniform. Also, in Maryland, a convicted felon successfully argued that requiring him to register as a sex offender was unlawful because his conviction occurred before the statute requiring registration was enacted.

My relative needs a caregiver who can drive. How can I make sure the person is a safe driver?

Your background check should include the caregiver's driving record if the worker will drive your relative to appointments and other outings. Driving records will provide information such as if the person has a valid license and any driving infractions. Each state determines who can access driving records, and the applicant may be the only person who can obtain a copy of this information. If so, ask the caregiver to provide a certified copy of their driving record.

At a minimum, caregivers who use their own cars to transport your parent should furnish proof of a valid license and automobile liability insurance. Note the expiration dates so that you will know when to request proof of renewal. Before you provide the caregiver with the use of a vehicle, contact your insurance company to see if the worker will be covered.

How can I ensure that the person I want to hire is legally authorized to work in the United States?

It is against the law to hire individuals who cannot legally work in this country. Anyone you hire—regardless of citizenship—must fill out the *employee* section of IRS Form I-9 (Employment Eligibility Verification) and submit documents to you verifying their identity and employment authorization. Refer to the last page of the I-9 for a list of acceptable documents. Employers must complete the *employer* section of Form I-9 attesting that they reviewed the documents and they appear genuine and pertain to the employee. The U.S. Department of Homeland Security requires employers to retain these records during employment and for a certain period of time after employment has ended. The rules regarding retention are posted on the website of the U.S. Citizenship and Immigration Services (see Resources).

Should I tell applicants that my parent is gay?

Unfortunately, discrimination still exists against members of the lesbian, gay, bisexual, and transgender (LGBT) community. Legally, your parent does not have to reveal their sexual orientation nor does a health provider have a right to ask.

Do I have to disclose that my parent has HIV or AIDS?

Most states encourage—but do not require—individuals who have HIV or AIDS to divulge their status to health care providers. Arkansas is an exception by making the failure to disclose having the virus prior to receiving medical treatment from a doctor or dentist a misdemeanor. Anyone providing medical or personal care should use universal precautions such as wearing gloves and safely disposing of waste, regardless. If you have questions about your parent's legal obligation to disclose, contact your local health department for guidance.

Even if your state does not require people to disclose their AIDS or HIV status to caregivers, doing so is worth considering. In the event that a worker accidentally comes in contact with your parent's infected blood or body fluids, the caregiver needs to know to seek treatment without delay. If you decide to inform the caregiver that your relative has HIV or AIDS, do not apologize for your parent's status and do not go into unnecessary detail.

Should I tell prospective caregivers that my parent is sometimes violent?

Yes. Abuse by clients is more prevalent than many people realize. The elderly sometimes threaten, punch, kick, and bite their caregivers, including family members. It is tempting to withhold unfavorable information about your parent for fear that applicants will turn down the job, but a failure to disclose could be used against you in court if the caregiver is injured while working. In California, a home health worker was in the kitchen washing a large knife when her eighty-five-year-old client, who had Alzheimer's, bumped into her and reached toward the sink. While attempting to restrain the client, the caregiver dropped the knife, which hit her wrist, causing her to lose feeling in several fingers. The caregiver sued the client and the client's husband for damages. The California Supreme Court ruled against the caregiver on the grounds that she had worked with Alzheimer's patients before and, therefore, should have known that aggressive behavior is not unusual and the husband—who had hired the caregiver—had warned her that his wife had combative tendencies. The caregiver, who came through an agency, was limited to benefits from her workers' compensation insurance.[x] Therefore, it is always best to let health care providers know if there is a possibility that your parent can be violent, even if such behavior rarely occurs. Also, if you know, share with caregivers what you think triggers your parent's aggression. Individuals with Alzheimer's sometimes exhibit a phenomenon, known as sundowning, which can cause behaviors such as violence, hallucinations, paranoia, restlessness, and confusion to occur in the early evening hours and at night.

My relative has a firearm. Should I inform agencies or caregivers I hire directly?

According to a Gallup poll[xi], thirty-three percent of adults over the age of sixty-five own a firearm in the United States. Many elderly individuals also suffer from dementia or other health issues that can cause paranoia, hallucinations, and confusion. In Florida, a geriatric care manager entered a home and was met by a client pointing a pistol at her. The client, who struggled with alcoholism, was angry that her daughter had taken her car away.[xii] These and other similar stories suggest that you should let caregivers know about firearms in the home for their protection as well as the safety of your parent.

Ideally, families should remove firearms from the home of seniors who are not responsible gun owners. Beware that taking away someone's gun can be just as serious as taking away the person's car keys. One day, I called my mother to tell her that I was stopping by after work. She told me to be careful entering the home because my father was walking around the house with his gun. Because of his dementia, he sometimes believed there were other people in the house and, at this moment, he was looking for them. This was a new behavior and my mother was understandably frightened and upset. My father kept his gun in the top drawer of his bureau so I felt sure that he would miss it if I ever took it. On the other hand, I felt that my mother's safety was paramount so I removed the gun and a box of ammunition from their home. I decided that if my father became angry, I would just have to deal with the repercussions. Through the grace of God, he never missed or mentioned the gun. Fortunately, the jurisdiction where he lived, as well as many other states, had a no-questions-asked firearm surrender program to encourage people to turn in guns, and that's exactly what I did with my father's pistol. My mother was very appreciative and I felt that I might have prevented a terrible tragedy.

Will caregivers work in a home with pets?

It depends. Inform agencies and applicants for private hire that your parent has a pet in the home. Some agencies and some caregivers provide pet care, such as feeding, walking, and cleaning cages and litter boxes, as part of their services. For others, the presence of pets is a deal breaker because of allergies or a dislike or fear of animals.

CHAPTER 3

CAREGIVER MANAGEMENT 101

Being the chief care coordinator for a relative is like running a small business. This may sound daunting, but this chapter will provide you with the information, tools, and strategies you need to successfully manage your caregiving operation.

My parent's caregiver starts work next week. What can I do to get ready?

As with most things in life, the more organized you are, the better things will go. To ensure a smooth start, I suggest preparing a written care plan for the aide. Care plans are not static documents and will change over time depending on your parent's condition. Therefore, it is important that caregivers review the care plan on a regular basis for updates. Generally, a care plan should include:

- the duties the caregiver is expected to perform
- a list of your parent's current health issues, dietary restrictions, allergies, past surgeries, assistive devices used (such as a cane or hearing aid), and doctors
- a list of people to contact in case of emergency
- a chart showing the name, dosage, frequency, purpose, and any special instructions for all medications your parent takes, including over-the-counter drugs. An example of a special instruction would be "Take with food." Clear, written directions are essential, especially if more than one caregiver is administering your relative's medications.

Here is an example of a medication chart:

MEDICATIONS				
Medication	Dosage	Frequency	Purpose	Special Instructions

If EMTs are ever called to your parent's residence, instruct the caregivers to provide them with a list of medications and a Do Not Resuscitate (DNR) order, if applicable. A DNR form instructs health care providers not to perform life-sustaining functions such as cardiopulmonary resuscitation (CPR) if the person stops breathing or their heart stops beating.

In addition to developing a written care plan, you should:

- stock up on items the caregiver will need such as medical supplies, adult briefs, clean sheets, towels, and wipes
- prepare a brief bio about your relative, including information about their interests, hobbies, talents, accomplishments, career, and religious practices. You want your parent's aide to see your loved one as more than just a job. Telling stories about your loved one is also useful, but your parent may have many different caregivers over the years and you want to ensure that information about their life is transmitted to everyone
- document your parent's likes and dislikes, favorite TV shows, and daily routines, such as reading the newspaper during breakfast. Note their habits, such as rising early or retiring late. What thermostat setting do they prefer? Does your relative prefer to keep their curtains closed all day? Include any pet peeves that your loved one has. Also, let the aide know if your parent is someone who always wants to look their best, especially when they go out of the house or

entertain visitors. This information will let your parent's caregiver understand the whole person and not just their caregiving needs.

In addition to the above suggestions:

- Purchase an inexpensive composition notebook for the caregiver to maintain a daily log, documenting the care they provide to your parent. The log should include, at a minimum, the dates and times medications were administered. I also recommend having the caregiver document the times certain tasks were performed, such as repositioning your parent or changing their dressing. This information will let the next caregiver know the next time these tasks should be repeated. If your relative uses a catheter, have the caregiver document the amount and color of your relative's urine output so that this information can be passed along to their doctor or nurse. Dehydration is a major problem with the elderly population. Be sure that the caregiver records the date when the catheter was last changed. Also, notes about visits from physicians and others involved in your parent's care should go in the logbook.
- Make an extra set of house keys, if necessary. Some caregivers let themselves into the home, depending on the client's mobility. Another option is to use a lockbox so you don't have to have new keys made each time you hire a new caregiver or an employee leaves. With a lockbox, you just change the combination. You may not want to give out house keys until you have gotten to know the caregiver well. It just depends on your parent's situation.
- Create a comfortable work environment for your parent's caregiver. Make sure that they have a well-cushioned chair with armrests to sit in. One of my mother's caregivers had to bring this issue to my attention. The chair I provided was armless with a bottom on the smallish side. Within twenty-four hours, the caregiver had a nice wingback chair with a

generous seat cushion. I really appreciated that the caregiver spoke up and let me know. It was something I had not thought of.

- Caregivers who care for a bedridden client appreciate an overbed table like those found in hospitals. These tables prevent back strain because caregivers do not have to bend over and stretch to reach supplies.
- Provide a TV in your parent's room for both your relative and their aide to watch.
- If you have Wi-Fi, consider giving your caregiver access if they ask.
- Protect your parent's wood furniture by placing a piece of glass or acrylic on top. Some people do not think to ask beforehand where to set their belongings and just choose the closest flat surface. They do not mean any harm, but you want to be proactive and prevent damage to your loved one's furnishings.

Are there additional considerations for live-in caregivers?

In order not to pay caregivers for the hours they spend sleeping, employers must provide live-in caregivers with "private quarters in a homelike environment."[xiii] If your parent's residence is not large enough to give the caregiver a separate bedroom, then the home must be arranged in a way that affords the aide as much privacy as reasonably possible. The caregiver's living quarters must be furnished with at least a bed (or cot, air mattress, or sofa bed) and dresser or closet. One exception to the private or separate quarters requirement is when the caregiver is a member of the family or household who was already living in the home prior to becoming a caregiver.

A homelike environment means that the caregiver must have access to a place to prepare and eat meals, a bathroom, and a place to relax. These areas can be shared with the client.

When my grandmother's caregiver agreed to move in and help with my mother, I asked about her favorite color and decorated her room in that color palette. I furnished the room with a bed, dresser, loveseat, cable TV, and linens. The caregiver also said that she loved to read so I added a bookcase. The room did not have a closet so I bought a portable closet off the internet so she could hang her clothes. After the caregiver arrived, we shopped for an area rug together.

Do I have to provide food for the caregiver?

Usually, non-live-in caregivers bring their own meals. There is no legal requirement that clients provide meals for live-in caregivers; however, some agencies include this stipulation in their contracts. A live-in caregiver you hire directly may expect meals or, at least, a meal allowance. Live-ins should be given some say about the kind of food they like, but they are responsible for purchasing specialty food items or food based on a restricted diet.

How do I handle my parent's concern about losing their privacy?

Their apprehension is perfectly understandable. The arrangement is intrusive by its very nature and affects all members of the household—the care recipient, spouses, children, etc.

One way to accept the reality that your parent's home or your home has become a small business with employees moving about is to focus on the many benefits that caregivers bring. It is the rare caregiver who does not offer helpful hints or lift everyone's spirits with their positive outlook. One caregiver cooked us a delicious meal that she learned to make from her mother in Sierra Leone. It is difficult having non-family members around constantly, but you will adapt quicker than you think.

After my husband and I moved my mother in with us, she had twenty-two-hour care daily. I reserved two hours every day so that I could have the house to myself. When we hired a live-in, my husband had to give up his art studio so that the caregiver could have a separate living area. I felt terrible about this, but we did not have another spare room in the house.

What should I go over with the caregiver on the first day or night on the job?

There are several steps you can take to acclimate the caregiver to their new job and new environment.

- Make the person feel welcome and let them know you are looking forward to having them help with your relative.
- Reintroduce the caregiver to your parent and then give the worker a mini-tour of your parent's home. Show them where to hang their coat. Let them know that they may put their meals in the refrigerator if they like, and point out the microwave and the recycling bin. Also, show the caregiver where they can eat meals, and point out which bathroom to use.
- Inform the aide where to park their car and mention any neighborhood parking restrictions. For example, Baltimore and the District of Columbia have a huge parking problem in certain residential areas. Their solution is to limit the number of hours that a vehicle not displaying an unrestricted parking permit can remain on the street without being ticketed or towed. The purpose of this policy is to ensure that people living in the area can find a parking space close to home. To accommodate residents who have caregivers, these cities provide renewable temporary parking permits for health care providers.
- Introduce the caregiver to other people who live in the home and explain their relationship to your parent. Tell the caregiver everyone's schedule, especially people who will be arriving late at night; otherwise, the aide may be startled to hear the door opening at odd hours.
- Go over the plan of care you developed. Most tasks will be clear but others may need more explanation or even require a demonstration. Do not assume that anything is obvious or

that people you hire will naturally do things the way you want them done. If the job calls for performing personal care tasks, this is a good time to mention any areas on your parent's body that might be particularly sensitive or painful.

- Tell the caregiver where medical supplies are stored.
- Show the caregiver how to use medical equipment and appliances they will be operating or monitoring.
- If housework is part of the job, show the caregiver where the cleaning supplies, broom, vacuum, and mop are stored.
- If the caregiver is responsible for taking out the trash, go over the trash pickup schedule.
- Show the caregiver where the first aid kit, fire extinguisher, and flashlight are kept.
- Provide names of family members and friends who have permission to take your parent outside of the home.
- Go over the house rules with the caregiver. You may have heard the expression "Start out the same way you want to end up." This means that you should set the tone and establish whatever guidelines you want at the beginning. Trying to change rules later may prove more difficult. An example of a house rule would be "no smoking."
- If you are the caregiver's employer, have them complete IRS Form W-4 to determine federal income tax withholding, IRS Form I-9 to verify that they are eligible to work in the U.S., and a state withholding form in states that have an income tax.
- Obtain emergency contact numbers so that you will know who to call in the unlikely event that the caregiver gets ill or has an accident. Encourage employees to speak up and ask questions at any time about anything. I really stressed this with my mother's caregivers. The last thing I wanted was for an aide not to admit when they were unsure or uncomfortable about something. Keeping the lines of communication open is key to any relationship and caregiving is no exception.

Also, remember that there will be a period of adjustment for all parties involved. Your loved one and you will get used to having non-family members in the home and the caregiver will get used to dealing with different personalities and new surroundings.

How should caregivers address my parent?

Most caregivers will address their clients by their last name or their first name preceded by a title such as Miss or Mrs. Some people with professional titles such as doctor may want their caregivers to address them as such. It is not unusual for caregivers from some cultures to refer to their female clients as "mama." While they may mean the reference as a term of endearment, I personally do not like it. If you don't either, just politely explain that you prefer for your parent to be addressed in a different manner. It is important to maintain professional boundaries and how people are addressed is part of this.

I've seen caregivers use baby talk with seniors. Is this acceptable?

Discourage caregivers from using baby talk, aka elderspeak, with your parent. Some examples are, "Let's take our bath now," "Good girl," and "Are we having a good day today, dear?" Elderspeak is condescending and inappropriate. A study conducted more than a decade ago of nursing home residents with dementia who were subjected to elderspeak found that the residents were more aggressive and less willing to comply with directives from the staff. Researcher Dr. Kristine Williams of the University of Kansas concluded that speaking in this demeaning manner to residents diminished their self-esteem.[xiv]

What steps can I take to have a positive relationship with my parent's caregiver?

- Treat your parent's caregiver with the respect, courtesy, and understanding they deserve.

- If your parent has serious or numerous health issues, your caregiver will feel appreciated if family members occasionally lend a hand. The caregiver should, of course, do the heavy lifting; that's what you pay them for. But there is no reason why relatives can't help out occasionally, especially if they are present and have the time. If your parent's caregiver gets the impression that the family doesn't care or doesn't want to be bothered, then the aide will stay out of their way and only involve the family when necessary. This could result in the caregiver not passing on valuable information about your loved one.
- Try to be as consistent as possible with the caregiver's hours and do not arbitrarily reduce them. These workers rely on their paychecks and they may look for a more stable assignment if you cut their hours often or arbitrarily. Of course, unforeseen issues come up and change is unavoidable. The point here is to be mindful that most workers need a steady paycheck rather than one that fluctuates on a whim.
- Make sure that the caregiver knows in advance about changes in your parent's schedule or routine. Keep a calendar in a prominent place that shows appointments with doctors, friends, and the hairdresser, for example.
- Encourage the caregiver to raise issues that cause concern even if they are not positive that a problem exists. Many caregivers, especially those from other countries, are reluctant to raise issues for fear that they will be blamed or to avoid unpleasantness. Reassure the worker that your parent and you need and want to hear all news—good and not so good.
- If your relative's personal aide has been working a while and is doing a great job, show your appreciation through small, simple, but thoughtful gestures. A thank-you card is thoughtful, and there are now specific greeting cards for caregivers. You can also nominate an outstanding caregiver for a Dementia Diplomat Care Award from the Dementia Society of America (see Resources). The award carries no monetary

value, but the caregiver will know the gesture came from the heart. If you go on vacation, bring them back a small souvenir. Hand-made gifts and home-baked goods that the caregiver can share with their family will also make them feel special. A monetary gift is always appreciated and can come in the form of cash, movie passes, a gas card, or a gift card to the caregiver's favorite store.

- Remember the caregiver on major holidays and on their birthday. It is not unusual to give caregivers a bonus at holiday time. The rule of thumb for a holiday gift at Christmas or Hanukah, for example, is one week's pay (the same as for a nanny), but anything you give is sure to be appreciated.
- Occasionally, check with the caregiver to see if the temperature in the home is comfortable for them. Everybody's different. Your parent's well-being is paramount, of course, but making minor adjustments, where possible, will show the caregiver that their comfort is important.

How can I know if the caregiver is treating my relative with dignity?

Treating someone with dignity is usually a matter of small, rather than grand, gestures. Below are some examples of respectful behaviors. Compare the actions of your parent's caregiver to see where they fall. Does the caregiver:

- greet your loved one each day and say goodbye at the end of the shift?
- ask your parent for permission to perform care tasks (e.g., "Would you like to take your bath now?")?
- tell your parent what they are going to do before they do it (e.g., "It's 3:00 p.m. I need to turn you on your back for a while.")?
- drape a towel or sheet over your relative when working on private areas to preserve your loved one's dignity and

prevent them from being embarrassed? This is especially required when other people are present, even if those others are healthcare professionals.

- talk to your relative even if they cannot respond or understand? Hearing is the last sense to go and the caregiver should not treat your loved one as if they are not aware of what is happening.
- compliment and encourage your parent?
- listen to your parent? If your loved one does not want to do something, the caregiver should try to find out why. Maybe the activity is painful or your parent does not fully understand what is about to happen.
- ask about removing bed covers if your parent appears hot or adding a blanket if your parent seems cold?
- adjust the thermostat as needed?
- air your parent's room out periodically?
- keep their cellphone use to a minimum?
- if your parent has a catheter, turn their urine bag inward when company comes in order to preserve your relative's dignity?

A lot of caregivers come from countries outside of the United States. What are some of the issues and challenges that may arise?

When the worker and client are from different racial, ethnic, or cultural backgrounds, there are more challenges, the biggest of which is communication. When the client and the caregiver do not speak the same language, the opportunity for miscommunication increases. The result can range from inconsequential to life-threatening. One way to minimize problems in this area is to ask caregivers if they have any questions after you have imparted new or complex information or changed your parent's routine. What you want to avoid is assuming that they understood without checking.

Some cultures favor speaking in a loud tone. If your parent prefers conversations be held at a quieter level, let the caregiver know in a polite way. In contrast, you may hire a caregiver from a culture where people speak softly and your family is loud. Your communication style can seem threatening and harsh. Because the caregiver needs a job, they will try to adjust to your family's communication style, but they may find it intimidating to be told "Speak up, we can't hear you." The bottom line is to be sensitive to differences among people.

Another issue that can arise occurs when people are not familiar with something. One morning, I asked a caregiver if she had put lotion on my mother after she gave her a bath. The caregiver said "Yes" and pointed to a cream that had an entirely different purpose. When I told the caregiver that what she used was not lotion and then explained the purpose of the other cream, she said that she did not know there was a difference. Another caregiver who worked for a friend of mine mistook the dirty clothes hamper for a trashcan and put soiled Depends in it. Just realize that there may be a steeper learning curve when the caregiver is not native-born.

My parent's caregiver is mostly a companion. What types of activities can they do together?

You want your parent's aide to suggest meaningful activities to do with your parent because mental stimulation is key to your relative's emotional well-being. The caregiver and your relative can play board and card games, work puzzles together, and take in-person or virtual tours of world-class museums such as the National Gallery of Art in Washington, D.C. and the National Museum of Modern and Contemporary Art in Seoul. If possible, going to activities outside of the home is great. Your parent will feel like they are still part of the community at large, and seeing new things will help keep them active and mentally alert.

I also involved my mother in small tasks around the house. She helped fold the laundry I took out of the dryer. This was fun as we would both take the end of a soft, warm sheet and fold it together. My mother also peeled vegetables and stirred the cornbread mix. She would often ask if there was something she could do because she wanted to be useful. In retrospect, I wish I had put more thought into finding ways for her to help.

What should my parent's caregiver wear?

A lot of caregivers wear scrubs because the apparel is comfortable, protective, and professional-looking. Some clients prefer caregivers to wear street clothes when the two of them leave the home so that the public cannot readily identify the person as a caregiver. If your relative's agency requires its workers to wear scrubs and your parent would feel more comfortable if the caregiver dressed as a friend or companion, ask the agency to make an exception. Your agency should not find this request unreasonable.

Do caregivers get breaks?

There is no *federal* law requiring employers to give caregivers breaks, but some agencies and private duty caregivers include meal and rest breaks as part of their contracts. Regardless, the caregiver should be allowed reasonable breaks, during which they are paid, as long as your relative's needs are met and they are able to summon the caregiver if they require assistance. Check to see if your *state* labor department mandates breaks for household employees.

Does the client pay the caregiver during meal periods?

The federal government describes a meal break as one lasting at least thirty minutes, under ordinary circumstances.[xv] The time is not considered compensable and employers do not have to count this period as hours worked. The exception is if the caregiver is expected to work or be available to work during their meal break. Only one of my mother's caregivers ever declared she was taking her lunch break and left my mother's room. All of the others chose to eat their meals while they were on duty. I offered to watch my mother while they took a break, but they always declined. You should contact your state labor board to see if employers pay for meal breaks under state law.

If the caregiver is not busy, are they available for other work that is not necessarily specific to my relative's needs?

Many clients operate under the misconception that if caregivers are not "busy," then they can be required to perform tasks not directly related to their client. This simply is not true. Moreover, such thinking is a quick way to lose your caregivers. Even if your parent sleeps for several hours straight, caregivers should not be given odd jobs that do not benefit the client. The caregiver is still considered to be on duty and engaged to wait, which means they are not available to polish the silver, weed the garden, or make the beds for overnight guests visiting for the holidays. The owner of a caregiver agency who was interviewed by *The Washington Post* spoke about a client's request for her parent's aide to mow the grass and another who "wanted us to grill for the family." As the owner succinctly put it, "Your home health-care aide is not your maid or party planner."[xvi]

The caregiver will have to shop for my relative. How should we handle the money?

Consider using a debit card linked to a separate account for this express purpose so that the caregiver only has access to a predetermined amount of funds. Require caregivers to provide receipts for all expenditures.

The caregiver during the night shift cannot stay awake to do their job. Is there anything I can do?

I wish I had good news, but finding a reliable caregiver for the graveyard shift is extremely difficult. Many workers have day jobs and they anticipate catching some shuteye during their night caregiving job. I would not have minded if the caregiver slept, as long as they woke up in time to tend to my mother as needed. Most, however, did not and it took me a long time to find reliable caregivers for this shift. I showed one worker how to set the alarm on her cellphone to go off every two hours so that she would wake up to check on my mother. Being a caregiver at night is also hard because the residence is dark and quiet and everyone else is asleep. The caregiver who ultimately worked out best could sleep at home during the day because her mother lived with her and helped out with her children. Otherwise, she also would have been too tired to do a good job. This is another area where there are no easy answers. You may have to go through a few aides before finding someone who can handle the night shift.

Also, caregivers who work at night may feel the need for more noise in order to stay awake and may want to keep both the lights and the TV on. They may assume that your parent, who may not appear to be aware of their surroundings, is not bothered by the light and the noise and has no objection. However, no one really knows what another person senses. Having the lights and TV on could make it difficult for your relative to sleep. Just remember that the residence belongs to them, not the caregiver, and the environment must always be maintained for your parent's comfort.

What should the caregiver do if my parent has to go to the hospital suddenly?

After calling 911, the caregiver should notify whoever is on the emergency contact list. The caregiver should give the first responders key information about your parent's health issues, medications your parent is taking, any allergies your parent has, and a DNR order, if applicable. The caregiver's agency should be notified and all privately hired caregivers should be instructed not to report to work until further notice. Keep them apprised of your relative's condition but realize that some workers may have to move on to other jobs. I had an aunt who was bedridden and who had numerous hospital stays each year. Her adult children found it impossible to keep caregivers because she was hospitalized sometimes for months at a time.

What should I do to prepare for an emergency?

Emergencies can be anything from power outages to natural disasters, such as wildfires and hurricanes. Have a backup plan. If the power is out for several days during extreme temperatures, the heat or cold may be too harsh for your parent to stay in their home. Lack of power is also problematic if your parent relies on medical equipment powered by electricity or if their medication needs to be refrigerated. If your loved one does not have a back-up power source, consider purchasing a generator. The hospice agency that we used had an arrangement with two nursing homes to accept the hospice clients in cases of emergency.

Following Katrina, the federal government implemented laws requiring Medicare- and Medicaid-certified facilities to have written plans and procedures for emergencies and to train their employees in these procedures. The same kind of planning is necessary for your parent, and the importance of having a plan increases if you are a long-distance care coordinator. The extent of your planning will be directly related to your loved one's condition and needs. Someone who is bedridden and on a ventilator is at a higher risk during an emergency than someone who is mobile and able to quickly move out of harm's way. You should have one plan in the event your parent and their caregiver have to shelter in place and another in case they have to evacuate. Evacuation involves additional considerations such as transportation and relocation. You also need to know in advance how you will transport your relative. Relocation can be extremely hard physically and mentally on older people. Sometimes, however, you do not have a choice and your parent must be moved to safety. If you think your parent may need to be evacuated, do not wait until the last minute. Other similarly situated people may need the same resources.

To safely shelter in place, below is a list of items your parent and the caregiver will need to have available for the duration of the emergency or until help arrives. It is difficult to predict how long an emergency will last. Therefore, select a reasonable period of time based on past events, if possible, and have sufficient supplies for that duration. The main goal is to ensure that your relative and the caregiver have a well-thought-out plan.

- non-perishable food and water
- can opener
- medication
- assistive devices, such as contact lens and dentures
- first aid kit
- medical supplies
- clothing, including underclothes
- flashlight
- blankets
- a means of communication
- batteries
- hand sanitizer
- ID, health insurance card, Social Security card, and healthcare directive
- telephone numbers of physicians, pharmacies, insurance company, hospice, etc.
- pet food, if applicable

If you use a caregiver agency, ask about their policy in the event of an emergency. Will the caregiver on duty remain with your parent if the worker for the next shift is unable to come to work? If you hire a caregiver directly, ask if they will be able to stay, if necessary. One agency I used said at the initial interview that, in the event of a snowstorm, for example, the caregiver on duty would stay past their shift until a replacement caregiver was able to come. Several months later when a snowstorm hit the area, their caregiver hightailed it out of my mother's house when the first few flakes began to fall. The caregiver said that she was afraid she would get "stuck" if she did not leave immediately. I let the agency know what happened and said that I did not want her back.

I'm hiring an additional caregiver. Is it permissible to ask my current caregiver to train the new person?

I always had new workers, regardless of their credentials, shadow one of my mother's experienced caregivers for a few hours before allowing the new caregiver to work on her own. I paid the new caregiver during this training period. Having current caregivers train new aides also helps them function better as a team.

What are some challenging situations that caregivers encounter?

One of the most common issues is what I call the "twofer." This situation arises when two individuals—usually, a husband and wife—expect the caregiver to assist both people even though they are only paying for help for one. A friend told me that her father's caregiver objected when his wife asked the caregiver to get her walker. The caregiver was right to object because she was not hired to assist the wife. Nor was the agreed-upon rate of pay based on caring for two people. If someone other than the client needs assistance, then it's up to the caregiver to decide to take on extra duties and, if so, they should be compensated for the additional work.

Another problem that caregivers encounter is working in homes where family members abuse their parent. It is difficult to see a vulnerable individual mistreated. Adult children sometimes verbally berate parents who suffer from dementia because the offspring are frustrated and/or erroneously believe that their parent is capable of doing better but is just not putting forth the effort. Neglect is also a form of abuse that can occur when family members do not have the requisite training. In these situations, caregivers can show family members the proper way to take care of their loved one.

In many states, caregivers are mandatory reporters of elder abuse, which means that the law requires them to contact Adult Protective Services or law enforcement when they witness or even suspect that a senior is being mistreated. Caregivers face several dilemmas in this situation, however. A lot of parents do not want to see their adult children get in trouble and, therefore, do not want anyone to contact the authorities. Second, some seniors are afraid that they will be taken from their home and placed in a facility if that is the only way to prevent further abuse. Caregivers are often reluctant to quit out of concern for the client. They feel that, without them as a buffer, the abuse would worsen. It can be a complicated position to navigate.

Another way to ensure that caregivers feel supported in the workplace is to make certain that family members speak and behave in a respectful manner. Please refrain from offensive behavior, such as using profanity or telling off-color, racist, or sexist jokes in the caregiver's presence. Caregivers are also put off when family members argue or disrespect one another in the caregiver's presence. I'm not talking about a spirited discussion or disagreement. It's the putdowns, sarcasm, name-calling, yelling, cursing, quarreling, door slamming, etc. that makes people feel uncomfortable. If the atmosphere is toxic enough, the caregiver could dread coming to work and will be anxious to leave at the end of the shift. Look at it from the caregiver's viewpoint: if you would hate to work in a tense or unpleasant environment, then so would they.

Another potential problem is being unfairly blamed when something goes wrong or when items come up missing. For example, it is not unusual for individuals with dementia to hide personal belongings for fear that someone will steal them, then forget that they hid the items and blame the caregiver. If you have experienced this type of behavior with your parent, you may want to give the caregiver the benefit of the doubt until you have more proof.

Caregivers also dislike working in an environment that is not clean, comfortable, and safe. Make sure your parent's home is tidy so the caregiver will feel at ease working there, using the bathroom and kitchen, and setting their belongings down. You don't want to go to a workplace that is filthy. Neither does the caregiver, and, furthermore, most caregivers will not stay in a home that has pests (roaches, mice, bedbugs, etc.).

Of course, your parent's home does not have to be the source of the problem. One caregiver told me about a previous job where another caregiver brought bedbugs into the client's residence. The first caregiver ended up transporting the insects to her home. Upon discovering the source of the problem, the caregiver threatened to quit, but, to prevent her from leaving, the client paid to have both the caregiver's entire apartment and his residence treated for bedbugs and terminated the caregiver who had introduced pests into both their homes.

Abuse by clients of caregivers is another, more serious problem, and is more prevalent than you may think. I have read and heard about clients hitting caregivers and calling them racial epithets.

Be considerate of the caregiver when it is time for their shift to end. Do not ask them to begin a task that will require staying late unless you are willing to pay overtime or allow them to come to work later on their next shift.

An additional irritant is not being provided with adequate supplies to do a good job. I know a caregiver whose client could not control his bowel movements or urination. He suffered from full-blown dementia and had given his neighbor financial power of attorney several years earlier. In exchange for his services, the neighbor was to inherit the man's home, which was in an exclusive neighborhood. At some point, the neighbor stopped purchasing latex gloves for the man's caregivers and they had to wrap plastic grocery bags around their hands to clean the client as best they could.

These scenarios are not made up but are real-life examples of what caregivers experience. If you do not want a high turnover among your parent's caregivers, then make sure that you take note of some of the many potential issues caregivers have to navigate.

My relative has diabetes but the caregiver allows foods that the doctor said are off-limits. What can I do?

Unless your relative does not have the mental capacity to understand which foods are bad for them, try not to blame the caregiver. Your parent may be strong-willed and they have the right to make decisions that are not in their best interest. It is important to recognize what caregivers can and cannot do with respect to their clients. If people with diabetes insist on eating foods that the doctor has warned against, there is little that a caregiver can do short of encouraging these individuals to follow their doctor's orders.

My parent's caregiver is always late. How should I handle this?

Know what you are not willing to tolerate and where you are willing to compromise. My mother had one caregiver who was consistently ten to fifteen minutes late for her shift, which began at 10:00 p.m. She was industrious and pleasant otherwise. Because I was still up when she arrived, her tardiness did not inconvenience me and she had other redeeming qualities.

In contrast, I terminated a caregiver who routinely arrived late for the morning shift, which began at 6:00 a.m. The schedule called for the night caregiver to let the morning caregiver in each day, but the latter's tardiness derailed the arrangement. This meant that I had to get up at 6:00 a.m. and wait for her to arrive so I could let her in. I did not want to pay the night caregiver overtime to stay until the morning caregiver arrived (which would have been the fair thing to do). Plus, no matter how dedicated a caregiver is, when their shift ends, that person is ready to call it quits and go home. Under the circumstances, the perennially late caregiver had to go.

I think my relative's caregiver is stealing pain pills. How should I address the problem?

Caregivers struggle with addiction just like workers in any other profession. Many certified nursing assistants lose their license because they steal their clients' drugs. It is not that difficult to steal medication, especially if a client is mentally impaired and there is little to no oversight from others. If your loved one is taking heavy pain medication such as oxycodone or Vicodin, make every effort to monitor the medication to make sure your loved one receives the prescribed dosages. In 2017, a Missouri home care aide was arrested after a hidden camera revealed she was switching her elderly client's hydrocodone tablets for the milder pain medication acetaminophen.[xvii]

Also, if another family member lives with your parent and that person has an addiction problem, the pain meds need to be locked away. When it comes to addiction, please check your naiveté and skepticism at the door. It may not be the caregiver who is stealing or switching your parent's medication. If, however, you suspect that the caregiver is the perpetrator, consider installing a surveillance camera. Just make sure that you comply with state law. Alternatively, you may decide to terminate the worker.

Two of my relative's caregivers do not get along. I don't want to take sides. Should I even get involved?

Multiple caretakers caring for one client is similar to job sharing. Fostering teamwork can be challenging because people's standards and way of doing things are not the same. However, the root cause is often one person believing that the other is not pulling their weight. For example, one caregiver claims that, when they arrive to take over, your incontinent relative always needs to be changed and the waste is not recent. The other caregiver disputes this account and insists that your relative was clean and dry when their shift ended.

If you have proof of the caregiver's allegation, then you can fire the worker whose performance fell short if the charge is serious enough. If the problem can be remedied, then let the worker know that what they did or didn't do cannot happen again. Or you may decide that additional training is needed, and, if so, put a plan in place. If no proof exists to corroborate the allegation, you should still raise the issue and increase your watchfulness. You do not want the caregiver to take any unacceptable behavior underground where it will be more difficult to detect. Having a caregiver know you are aware of their possible dereliction of duty may be sufficient. Obviously, you want caregivers to speak up when they see a problem, but do not rely on them alone to alert you.

Another issue that can arise is determining which caregiver is responsible when something goes wrong or an item is missing. Sometimes, it just isn't possible to get to the truth. In that case, you need to try to find a solution that puts your parent's well-being first and is fair to all caregivers involved. What you don't want to do is ignore problems between caregivers and hope they will go away.

If I have a problem with the caregiver the agency provided, should I discuss it with the caregiver directly or involve the agency?

First, speak to the caregiver directly if something is not being done to your satisfaction. As long as you speak to people in a pleasant, clear, but firm tone, they will usually respond in a positive manner. Address problems as they come up and don't wait until several have accumulated. Letting problems pile up and then addressing them all at one time can make workers feel defensive and angry.

I am thinking about terminating my parent's caregiver. What's the best way to handle it?

Keeping someone in a job that is not a good fit is not doing that person a favor. If a caregiver is not performing to your satisfaction, bring the problem to the caregiver's attention in a tactful manner.

Be specific about your concerns and, where applicable, ask if there is anything you can do or provide to help the caregiver improve. There is no need to belittle another person, ever.

If you ultimately make the decision to terminate your relative's caregiver and they are employed by an agency, inform the agency so they can find a replacement. Let the agency deliver the news to the caregiver that they will not be coming back. If the caregiver is someone you hired directly, you can terminate the worker in person or over the telephone. I have used both methods. Everyone I discharged was fired for cause, usually chronic lateness. I even pushed back the starting time for one caregiver in the hope that she would be able to get to work on time. She agreed an extra hour would make all the difference in the world and she would not have any further difficulty. When she continued to show up late, I terminated her at the end of her shift. Here are eight suggested steps to follow:

1. Let the caregiver know their services are no longer needed.
2. Briefly explain to the worker why, in your opinion, things did not work out.
3. Express regret that the arrangement has ended, if appropriate.
4. Thank the caregiver for their services to date, if applicable.
5. Handle administrivia, such as retrieving the house key.
6. Hand the caregiver their last check or let them know when to expect the last payment for services rendered.
7. Wish the worker all the best, if appropriate.
8. Keep it short and sweet.

Do not terminate caregivers abruptly except for cause or unforeseen circumstances. Remember, they may have a family to support and are counting on continued employment. Also, it could be months before another assignment comes along for them. This is not your problem, but it doesn't hurt to think about how your actions affect someone else.

My relative's caregiver wants to eat their meals in my relative's bedroom. I am not comfortable with this because it can attract bugs. How should I handle this issue?

While it is important to try to accommodate your caregiver, it is perfectly reasonable for you to take whatever steps you feel are necessary to keep the premises pest-free. Limiting where people may eat food in the home is one way to accomplish this. Or, if you or your relative simply are not on board with people eating food throughout your home, let the caregiver know where they may take their meals.

My caregiver is having childcare issues and has asked if they can bring their child to work. How should I respond?

Some situations do not have easy answers. I, personally, would be reluctant to allow a caregiver to bring their child to work because I would want all of the aide's attention focused on my parent. However, it would depend on the age of the child. I might allow an infant, but I would be more reluctant to approve bringing a toddler to a caregiving job. The caregiver cannot watch their child constantly and I would be concerned about liability issues if the child is injured on the premises. Having said that, however, such a request should not be dismissed out of hand. Small children often delight seniors and having a young person around might lift your parent's spirits. Your parent might even enjoy interacting with the child by reading stories and playing games together. Workers experiencing childcare problems might do a better job if they are not worrying about said issues. One of my mother's caregivers told me that she once worked as a live-in caregiver in the United States while her mother took care of her child in another country. When this arrangement fell through, the client allowed the caregiver to bring her child to reside in the home. I know firsthand that this caregiver was exceptional and I imagine that the family decided to do whatever it took to keep her. The bottom line, therefore, is that the answer depends on how valuable the caregiver is to your parent and if accommodations can be made in a safe manner that works for everyone involved.

My parent's caregiver asked to borrow money. They're a fantastic caregiver. Should I lend them money?

It is only natural to be sympathetic, but, in most instances, it is not a good idea to lend money to someone who works for your family. You need to manage expectations when it comes to favors, especially those of a monetary nature. First, the likelihood that the caregiver will be able to repay a loan is low. Second, be aware that the caregiver may disappear or may ask for money again a few months later.

If a caregiver provides excellent care for your relative, you may decide to take a chance. In five years of using caregivers, only one person ever asked me for money. Less than six months after my mother passed, the caregiver asked for money outright, not a loan. The caregiver did not specify an amount. I told her that I had to think about it and I would get back to her. She was an outstanding caregiver and I knew that she might not get another assignment for some time. After my mother passed, I gave her and my mother's other caregivers a generous monetary token of appreciation for all that they had done so I was somewhat surprised at her request. After much soul searching with my husband, I called her back a couple of days later and offered a sum that we were comfortable with. Perhaps the amount we offered was too low because the caregiver said that she would get back to me. I never heard from her again, which is unfortunate. I would have loved to stay in touch and recommend her to others, but her request, and, I guess, my response made things awkward.

Also, requests for financial assistance come in many forms. You may be asked to co-sign a lease or co-sign for a car so that the caregiver can get to work. I would strongly advise against co-signing for anything.

Am I liable if a caregiver is injured on the job?

Caregiving can be hazardous work and sometimes workers sustain injuries. If you hire aides directly and do not have employer's liability and workers' compensation insurance, and a caregiver is injured in the course of their duties, you may be liable for medical expenses, lost wages, and damages. Paying workers under the table may save you money, but you could lose a great deal more in the end. Few workers want to sue their employer but if they are injured on the job and cannot work for a significant period of time, they may feel that they have no other choice. If you hire through an agency, make sure the agency provides home health care insurance and workers' compensation insurance for its workers.

What is the difference between workers' compensation and employer's liability insurance?

Workers' compensation insurance covers workers who become injured or ill in the course of their employment, regardless of fault. Policies cover medical expenses and partial loss of income while the person is unable to work, up to the maximum amount set by the state where the employee works. Most states require employers to carry workers' compensation insurance; however, some states exempt certain employers such as those with fewer than a specified number of employees. Workers' compensation insurance does not cover pain and suffering.

Employer's liability policies provide insurance against lawsuits brought by injured or ill employees who are not satisfied with what they received from workers' compensation or lawsuits brought by a related third party, such as a spouse. To prevail, plaintiffs must prove negligence on the part of the employer. Some standard homeowner insurance policies do not cover in-home workers, but you may be able to purchase coverage separately. Workers' compensation and employer's liability insurance are often purchased together at the same time.

What records am I required to keep?

You are required to keep records for any caregiver who qualifies for minimum wage and/or overtime pay. Specifically, you are required to maintain the following information for each employee:

- full name
- home address
- number of hours worked each workday
- total number of hours worked each workweek
- total amount of wages paid each workweek
- total amount of overtime wages paid

There is no particular format you have to use. When the caregiver works the same regularly scheduled hours, you can prepare a set schedule and just have the caregiver put a check mark or initials indicating that they worked the scheduled hours. Also, you can give the employee the responsibility of preparing timesheets as long as the information is turned in to you.

You do not have to keep records on employees who qualify for the companionship exemption but it is a good idea to do so as a matter of course. The Fair Labor Standards Act (FLSA) defines companionship as “fellowship and protection for an elderly person or person with an illness, injury, or disability who requires assistance in caring for himself or herself.” Under federal law, companion caregivers are exempt from the federal government’s overtime and minimum wage requirements. Since you never know if the government or the caregiver will successfully challenge the exemption, it is best to keep payroll records.

With live-in caregivers, employers must also keep a copy of any contract they have with the employee.

How long does an employer have to keep payroll records?

The length of time is specified under FLSA.

My relative's caregiver was hired through an agency and we need them to work additional hours. Is it permissible for me to arrange the extra work with the caregiver directly? They are willing to work for a lot less than I pay the agency.

While it is tempting to save money by doing an end run around the agency, first check your agency agreement for prohibitory language about direct hiring. Violating the terms of the agreement could result in the agency terminating your contract altogether. Also, ask yourself if you are prepared to take on the responsibilities of an employer because that's what you would become if you hire the caregiver directly.

What's the best way to pay caregivers?

I recommend paying by check or direct deposit so that you will have a record of all payments made. Paying in cash requires you to keep large sums of money in the house, which can be unsafe. My mother's caregivers had to have bank accounts because the payroll service that I used paid them through direct deposit. Nowadays, with mobile banking apps, depositing checks couldn't be easier.

My parent plans to fly to visit relatives in another state and the caregiver will accompany them. Is the caregiver paid round-the-clock for the duration of the trip?

According to the U.S. Department of Labor, clients do not have to pay caregivers for hours worked outside of their regular schedule as long as the aide is "completely relieved from duty." This means, for example, not helping the client to the restroom and not pushing the client's wheelchair through the airport. Otherwise, the caregiver is working and has to be paid.

My parent is on morphine. Can caregivers administer narcotics?

Some states and some caregiver agencies have strict rules about who can dispense medication. Therefore, if you use an agency, their rules will apply. If you hire a caregiver directly, ask if the person is comfortable administering morphine. Many caregivers do not want this responsibility because they do not want to be blamed for accidentally giving too much. There is a delicate balance between giving enough morphine to numb someone's pain and giving so much that the person overdoses and dies. I was the only person who administered morphine to my mother.

My relative is receiving hospice care. What should the caregiver do if my relative has to go to the hospital or if they pass?

The caregiver should contact the family first, who in turn will contact the hospice agency. If the family cannot be reached, the caregiver should notify the hospice agency that their client has gone to the hospital or has passed. Upon admission into hospice, the family will usually be asked for the name of the funeral home their loved one wants to use.

It is not unusual for a caregiving assignment to transition from assisting with ADLs to hospice care. This is a difficult time for everyone, including caregivers. Because of their experience, they often know when the end is near long before family members do. Allowing the caregiver to be present for the transition can be important to both the client and the caregiver. My mother's primary caregiver was Muslim and asked to wash her body before calling the funeral home or the hospice agency. Washing the body is a ritual in her religion and this act was important to the caregiver who had tenderly cared for my mother for more than a year. Of course, I agreed. It was the least I could do and I was deeply touched by this final gesture.

My parent died and I no longer have a need for a caregiver. It seems strange to just abruptly end the relationship. Is there anything special that I need to do?

It is good to identify the need to handle the end of a caregiver's tenure with sensitivity. Often the bond between caregiver and client is deeper than most people realize. Invite the caregiver to your parent's funeral or memorial service. At my mother's funeral service, I asked her caregivers to stand and I publicly thanked them for taking such good care of her and for the support they provided to my husband and me. To this day, I stay in touch with several of them through holiday cards, telephone calls, and occasional lunches.

I have met many people who said inviting caregivers to the service for their parent never occurred to them. In other words, they considered the caregiver's job to be over once their parent passed. You will have a lot of preparations to make after your loved one passes, but remember that caregivers have shared many intimate moments with your parent and they are grieving too. Also, your loved one's caregivers will never return to your parent's home again which was their place of employment. Caregivers will wake up the next morning with nowhere to go. They have lost not only the companionship that they shared with your parent, but also their source of income. If the worker is a live-in, they have to pack up their belongings and move out, perhaps abruptly.

Consider sending each caregiver a card thanking them for their service and devotion (if that is how you feel). Do not just call the agency and say that the caregiver's services are no longer needed. Many families give caregivers a monetary gift, depending on the length of service. Any amount given is sure to be appreciated because it could be months before these workers find another assignment.

CHAPTER 4

LONG-DISTANCE CAREGIVING

Millions of family caregivers in the United States provide long-distance care for a loved one. This arrangement can be challenging for so many reasons—you may have to vet caregiver applicants over the telephone or over the internet and if there's an emergency and you need to fly to get to your parent right away, the price of a last-minute plane ticket can be exorbitant. Under these circumstances, it is only natural that the usual feelings of frustration, helplessness, and guilt are often intensified for long-distance caregivers.

Another major issue facing long-distance caregivers is how to stay connected to their loved one. If you cannot be physically near your parent and you have determined that they need professional caregiving, you can still coordinate their care despite the distance. Sympathetic friends and neighbors, and technology and services that target seniors, can all help you manage. The specific assistance that your parent needs will determine the type and amount of support required. This chapter aims to help ensure that you can stay sufficiently connected despite distance.

I live hundreds of miles from my relative. How can other people help me care for them long-distance?

When it comes to long-distance care, it is vital that you assemble a reliable support network. Managing someone's care is ten times harder if you attempt it alone. Relatives, friends, and neighbors who live near your parent may be able and willing to help, and the importance of having trusted individuals regularly visit your loved one cannot be underestimated. You need to know how your parent is being treated and if they are receiving proper care. A local support team of individuals who live close by can be a godsend by doing everything from serving as your eyes and ears, to keeping your parent company, providing transportation to their appointments, cutting grass, cutting wood, shoveling snow, et cetera.

Relying on neighbors can work out beautifully—or the arrangement can have disastrous unintended consequences. Some people, unfortunately, take advantage of older people's trust. Take the case of a married couple in Milwaukee who began looking after their ninety-two-year-old neighbor, a retired single schoolteacher with dementia. Within a few months, the couple had convinced or coerced their neighbor to sign a quitclaim deed transferring her home to them. They also began helping themselves to the almost two million dollars she had in various banks because she had signed a power of attorney, giving one of the men control of her finances.[xviii]

The Village Movement

The Village Movement is a grassroots member-based support network of neighbors that began in Boston to help seniors age in place. There are now villages across the United States and in Australia. Local organizations charge a membership fee in exchange for services, such as transportation to and from appointments, prescription pickup, wellness calls, technology assistance with computers and cellphones, and minor home repairs such as replacing a lightbulb. Villages also vet and recommend contractors, secure senior discounts, and provide opportunities for socialization. Local programs are supported by the Village to Village Network, a national organization that provides guidance, resources, and advocacy. To find the closest village near your loved one, check the Village to Village Network website (see Resources).

Lotsa Helping Hands

Lotsa Helping Hands (see Resources) is a website that allows care coordinators, such as yourself, to post requests for assistance to a private "community" of family, friends, and neighbors who have volunteered to help a specific individual—in this case, your parent. The service is free and people only respond to those requests that they are willing to do, or they can just send messages of support. The program can also send reminders about upcoming events in your parent's life, and you have the option of posting updates about their health. This feature can be especially helpful for those who do not have time to make a lot of telephone calls and answer the same questions.

Geriatric Care Managers

Hiring a geriatric care manager, also known as an aging life care professional, is one possible solution when you are managing your parent's care long-distance. These consultants don't all offer the same services, so you need to know what your parent's specific needs are. Below is a list of typical services:

- Helping determine your parent's in-home care needs and locate appropriate caregivers
- Scheduling and coordinating caregivers
- Making home visits to see how the caregivers are working out
- Connecting your parent with local services and resources for long-term care
- Coordinating medical care from routine doctor visits to emergency hospitalization
- Paying bills
- Arranging transportation to and from appointments
- Arranging for meal delivery
- Managing prescriptions
- Hiring housecleaners
- Facilitating communication among the client, family, and doctors

- Helping families resolve internal conflicts about long-term care for a parent
- Making vendor referrals and overseeing home repairs
- Conducting a home safety inspection
- Making sure your parent has necessary legal documents such as a power of attorney and health care directive
- Resolving disputes with care providers and insurers

In addition to the services listed above, some consultants have a specialized expertise in Medicaid, such as protecting assets and applying for benefits. You may opt to use a geriatric manager to manage all aspects of your parent's care or proceed à la carte by selecting specific services. They charge by the hour—between fifty and two hundred dollars on average—but many professionals offer a flat rate for their services. Some also charge for their initial consultation.

Concierge Services

Concierge services for the elderly help seniors with their non-medical needs. They provide many of the same services as geriatric care managers, but the latter are more likely to have a social work or health-related background. Individuals in the elder concierge industry come from more varied fields. A healthcare background is not necessary for many of the tasks concierge services provide, and you may want to compare their rates to what the aging care professional would charge. Concierge managers usually charge by the hour or in blocks of time. Some companies charge a monthly membership fee as well. Concierge managers often perform many services themselves, such as shopping, running errands, or accompanying clients to outings. Remember that if you use any service that involves risk or liability, find out if the people performing the service are insured and bonded. For assistance, search the internet for senior concierge services in your parent's area.

Daily Money Managers

A daily money manager (DMM) can manage your loved one's personal banking needs and help organize their financial affairs. These professionals offer the following services: bill paying, making bank deposits, monitoring bank and credit card accounts for fraudulent activity, tracking medical insurance claims, organizing medical insurance and tax documents, and handling disputes with vendors. Some DMMs prepare payroll for household employees, such as caregivers. A word of caution: DMMs are not substitutes for accountants or lawyers. While no state-issued license is required to practice, the American Association of Daily Money Managers will certify individuals who have completed fifteen hundred hours of study and passed an exam. Visit their website (see Resources) to find a DMM located near your parent. Many DMMs offer a free consultation to assess if their services can be of use.

Payroll Service

As discussed in a previous chapter, I used a payroll service to pay my mother's caregivers and file all of the required tax documents with the federal and state governments. All I had to do each week was call in the number of hours each person had worked. A payroll service could work well in a long-distance care situation.

Area Agencies on Aging

There are over six hundred Area Agencies on Aging (AAA) across the country. Established in 1973 under the existing Older Americans Act, these organizations help seniors age in place by coordinating and supporting a wide array of services delivered by both public AAAs as well as private contractors. Examples include: meal delivery, transportation, in-home health care, and homemaker services. Check the website of the National Association of Area Agencies on Aging (see Resources) for your loved one's nearest program.

Program of All-Inclusive Care for the Elderly (PACE)

PACE programs are run by non-profit organizations that contract with the government to provide Medicaid and Medicare services primarily to elderly individuals who are aging in place. Some of the services that PACE organizations provide include meals, personal care, adult day care, mental health counseling, social work, prescription drugs, authorized over-the-counter medications, medically necessary transportation, assistive medical devices such as walkers and hearing aids, physical, occupational, and recreational therapy, and hospice care.

Once enrolled, an interdisciplinary team develops an individualized plan of care and coordinates with the client's family to implement and manage the plan. PACE programs reassess clients on a regular basis and adjust services as needed. For example, personal care aides are not provided initially around the clock, but if a senior becomes frail enough to require such coverage, the program may increase the number of hours. If a PACE client needs to move into a nursing home at some point in the future, the program will cover the costs. Typically, PACE programs contract with specific nursing homes, but if the client does not want to go to these facilities, the person may opt out of PACE and use Medicaid benefits to pay for the nursing home of their choice.

To qualify for PACE, an individual must be at least fifty-five years old, eligible for Medicaid, Medicare or both, require a nursing home level of care, and reside in an area that is serviced by a PACE organization. Those who qualify through Medicare only must also be willing to accept Part D for their prescription drug coverage. According to the National PACE Association, most participants qualify for Medicaid and only a tiny fraction are private pay clients. Participants may opt out of PACE at any time.

Most participants do not pay anything for PACE services because the majority of participants qualify for Medicaid. Individuals who are eligible for Medicare only may have to pay out-of-pocket for some services. Cost of services is determined by the state and, in some cases, by each county.

As of 2021, only thirty states have PACE programs. Some states such as California have several centers. Maryland's sole PACE program is affiliated with Johns Hopkins University but the state is planning to expand the program to other geographical areas. You can find a list of PACE organizations by state on the Medicare website or on the website of the national association for PACE (see Resources). Some states refer to these types of managed care programs as Living Independence for the Elderly or LIFE programs.

What are some options for keeping my parent socially engaged with the family despite distance?

Concern for your parent's physical condition can be so all-encompassing that it is easy to overlook their emotional health, yet we all know that staying connected to family and friends is critical to a senior's physical and mental well-being. Research has shown that seniors who socially interact with others on a regular basis enjoy better health and perhaps even live longer than those who do not. In recent years, advancements in technology have made it easier than ever for people to stay connected.

Many seniors today are using interactive services such as FaceTime, Skype, email, and texting to stay in touch with family members and to prevent feelings of loneliness and depression. You can preprogram your parent's cellphone with numbers of family members, friends, doctors, etc. and put frequently called individuals on speed dial.

Special tablets for elders such as Grandpad facilitate communication and share information and photos among family members. Grandpad uses a simpler interface to allow seniors to call, text, and take and receive photos, and the device features large buttons instead of requiring users to type instructions.

For people caring for a loved one residing in another country who find international calls too expensive, one possible solution is WhatsApp, a free service that provides voice, text, messaging, videos, group chat, and photo sharing.

If your relative does not know how to access or navigate social media sites, give them some lessons, enlist the aid of a tech-savvy grandchild, or look for free or low-cost classes at a nearby senior center. Computer training for elders is a big thing now and many senior centers offer classes just for this age group. Also, businesses that specialize in helping seniors use computer technology are springing up. One such company, Visual Senior, will go to a senior's home and bring all of the equipment required for video calls between the senior and their family. Family members initiate all sessions and the elderly person's tablet opens up automatically when a call comes in. Many of these companies are small and only serve local markets, but it doesn't hurt to check around.

Then there are voice-activated products that initiate telephone calls, send voice messages, and respond to direct queries, such as, "What is the current temperature?" or "Who was president of the United States in 1920?" With additional applications, these products can do a lot more to assist seniors and keep them engaged.

How can my parent continue to be part of a larger community?

Senior Centers

Senior centers are a great place to meet other people and participate in activities ranging from mahjong to pickleball. The centers schedule outings to museums, movies, restaurants, malls, and casinos, and offer lessons in driver safety, art, and exercise. Some centers have a gym. One center in Montgomery County, Maryland loans medical equipment for pennies a day, has a weekly Ask the Pharmacist Day, and sponsors various support groups. Senior centers also offer diverse programs tailored for specific ethnic communities. Most activities are free, and some centers serve lunch at a reduced cost. Also, many centers provide pick-up and drop-off services to bring seniors to the center.

Senior Centers Without Walls

Spread across the country are community-based programs for seniors who have difficulty leaving their home. Many of these centers do not have a brick-and-mortar presence, and seniors use a telephone or computer to call in at a designated time to engage with other people about topics of mutual interest or simply to offer support to each other. Some centers hold activities at various free sites throughout the community, such as libraries and churches. To find a program, search online in your parent's geographical area for Seniors Without Walls.

Adult Day Care Centers

Adult day care centers have been around for decades and are increasing in number as the population ages. Adults get to socialize and participate in various programs and forms of recreation in a structured environment under the supervision of staff. Some centers specialize in specific populations, such as individuals with dementia.

Adult day care represents a viable alternative for families who want their loved one to have mental, social, and physical stimulation during the day. If you investigate adult day care for your parent, do your research. Find out what specific services they offer, if the center is licensed, and how long the facility has been in business. Also, ask about the background and training of the staff, if the program conducts background checks, the staff-to-client ratio, if the center provides pick-up and drop-off transportation, and the cost. At some centers, participants must be able to toilet themselves or bring someone with them to assist, while the staff at other centers provide help when needed. One place I considered for my mother required a written release from her primary physician to enroll, as well as a negative TB test. An in-person visit is a must before you put your loved one in an adult day care program. The air-conditioning was turned up so high at one center I visited during the summer that the seniors were all wearing heavy coats, scarves, and hats. Needless to say, that program did not make my cut.

Places of Worship

If your loved one visits a house of worship, ask what services they provide for elderly members of their congregation. Many places will transport members to service, take them home, and take communion to its homebound members.

GoGoGrandparent

There are few losses as hard for seniors to accept as the freedom to drive. The elderly see driving as the last bastion of independence and are loathe to relinquish the keys. Car services, such as Uber and Lyft, provide pick-up and drop-off services which can be scheduled online or via the company's app. Enter GoGoGrandparent, a service that lets seniors speak to a live operator to arrange Uber and Lyft rides or use telephone prompts if they are comfortable with that option. GoGoGrandparent is available nationwide and drivers can transport passengers within a radius of one hundred miles. You can register your parent on their website (see Resources).

Online Services

Fortunately, there are many tasks that lend themselves to automation in today's computerized world, such as online bill paying, automatic prescription refills, and automatic renewal of print subscriptions. Moreover, you can order groceries online for your relative on sites like Instacart and have them delivered to their home. Stores usually charge a markup for delivery service.

Wellness Check-in Services

Several fee-based services will call subscribers on a regular basis to conduct a general wellness check and give medication and appointment reminders. Calls are sometimes computer-generated and, if there is no answer after a predetermined number of attempts, the company will alert a designated family member or friend. In 2018, Maryland began a free program that offers one wellness call per day to participants to check on their well-being. Other states may offer a similar service.

What can I do to make sure that my parent's home is not hazardous?

A safe environment is paramount to your relative's well-being and each time you visit, you will need to ensure that items or situations that pose a danger are removed. Below is a list of steps you can take to reduce the likelihood of an accident:

- Ensure bathtubs and shower floors are non-skid.
- Install grab bars in the bathrooms.
- Remove scatter rugs. According to the Consumer Product Safety Commission, floors and flooring materials contribute to over two million injuries from falls per year.[xix]
- Install smoke detectors. Working smoke detectors reduce the risk of dying in a house fire by at least fifty percent. Either change the batteries every six months to a year or purchase long-life units with sealed batteries. These detectors last for ten years and are tamper-proof.
- Place a fire extinguisher in the kitchen.
- Install carbon monoxide detectors on every floor. Change the batteries every year.
- Eliminate poor lighting.
- Ensure that the light switch is near each door so that your parent does not have to enter a dark room and search for the switch.
- Make sure kettles and irons have an automatic shutoff.
- Remove clutter to prevent tripping.

- Keep pathways free of electrical and telephone cords.
- Check handrails to make sure they are sturdy.
- Tighten or discard loose legs and joints on furniture.
- Ensure that a flashlight is within your parent's reach from their bed.
- Install ground-fault circuit interrupters in areas in the home near water, such as kitchen and bathroom sinks. These devices protect against electrical shock when plugging in appliances.
- Make sure that clutter, solvents, and paints are not close to open flames, such as a furnace pilot light.

If you are unable to personally perform a home safety assessment, consider hiring a geriatric care manager or occupational therapist to handle this task. Also, many local fire departments will conduct a free fire safety inspection of private residences. Some even provide free smoke detectors and install them. Finally, AARP publishes a free online "Home Fit Guide" with tips to help you assess a home for "comfort, safety, and livability" and the Centers for Disease Control provide a similar brochure entitled "A Home Fall Prevention Checklist."

Wandering from home is not unusual behavior for people suffering from Alzheimer's and other forms of dementia. Today, there are tracking devices that people prone to wander can wear. This assistive technology is helpful in notifying family members when their loved one is out of range. Some devices even provide the exact location of the person. Other sensors emit an alert if the senior gets out of bed or opens the front door or if no movement at all has been detected for a specified period. And don't forget personal emergency response systems that allow seniors to call for help with the press of a button. Everyone remembers the "I've fallen and I can't get up" TV ads about a medical alert device that ushered in this new technology decades ago.

How can I monitor and manage my relative's medical needs from a distance?

You may not be able to accompany your loved one to their medical appointments, but you can still keep abreast of their condition, diagnoses, treatment options, and medication. Ask their doctor to set up a videoconference during their appointments so you can participate in real time. Today, many doctors offer their patients a portal or secure website to access their medical records, test results, medication schedules, office visit summaries, and more. Make sure you have a signed release form from your parent or other written authorization, such as a power of attorney, that permits healthcare providers to share patient medical information with you.

If you manage your parent's medication, look into automatic prescription refills, pill dispensers, and medication reminder systems such as RxmindMe. More than half of seniors take five or more different prescription drugs, and it can be challenging to keep track. Some devices emit a sound or flash of light to alert the senior when it is time to take a pill. Others send a text if a dose is missed and let the designated care coordinator know when it is time to refill a prescription. There are also monitors that capture a person's blood glucose, heart rate, weight, and sleep patterns, to name a few. The use of these "self-care" devices is expected to grow in the coming years as people become more health conscious and the prevalence of chronic diseases increases. A helpful site to check for reviews and ratings of these and other products that are particularly useful for the elderly is Tech-enhanced Life (see Resources).

Upon request, some pharmacies will provide a "bubble pack" containing an individual's prescriptions and incorporate the person's over-the-counter medications, if prescribed. The pills are grouped by time of day such as morning, noon, evening, and bedtime for a week, twenty-eight days or thirty-one days, usually. Each group of pills is individually sealed under clear plastic on a card. Bubble packs eliminate the need for sorting and counting out pills and show at a glance if the senior has taken their medication. Some pharmacies charge a fee for this service and bubble packs are not available at all pharmacies.

What kind of documentation do I need to have on hand for long-distance care?

You should keep a copy of your parent's Social Security card, birth certificate, insurance policies, marriage certificate or divorce decree, durable power of attorney, advance directive, and will or trust. Some of the long-term care services discussed in this book—such as Medicaid—are income-based and, to qualify, your parent will have to demonstrate that they meet the financial criteria. If the need arises, you will also need documentation regarding your parent's assets and income.

CHAPTER 5

ABUSE

A man hires a caregiver to help take care of his wife. The wife dies and the caregiver begins caring for the husband who is in his late eighties and beginning to suffer from dementia. Over the course of the next two years, the caregiver steals hundreds of thousands of dollars from the man's bank accounts. She is eventually convicted and sentenced to five years in prison. The caregiver used much of the stolen money to purchase designer clothing and accessories at high-priced stores and to buy her daughter a luxury car.[xx]

Each year, at least ten percent of all adults sixty-five years of age or older are abused.[xxi] Because over ninety percent of seniors live in the community, most abuse occurs outside of a nursing home or other institutional setting.[xxii] Individuals who live alone are the most at risk, along with people whose family members do not or cannot visit them on a regular basis.

These statistics are not meant to alarm you. Most professional caregivers would never harm or exploit a vulnerable individual. In fact, most perpetrators of elder abuse are family members, such as spouses and adult children, who take advantage of their close familial relationship with the victim.[xxiii] However, caregiver abuse *does* occur, and, as your parent's care coordinator, you need to know how to reduce the risk of abuse for your loved one.

The most effective way to prevent abuse is to do your due diligence before you hire a caregiver and to remain observant once having done so. This chapter will show you how to accomplish this, as well as how to recognize the signs of abuse and who to contact for help if you discover or even suspect your parent is a victim.

What is elder abuse?

Each state has its own definition of elder abuse. The federal government defines the term as "an intentional act, or failure to act, by a caregiver or another person in a relationship involving an expectation of trust that causes or creates a risk of harm to an older adult."[xxiv] Abuse can be overt, such as assaulting someone, or subtle, like ignoring someone's needs. Most elder abuse falls into the following categories:

- physical
- emotional
- neglect
- financial
- sexual

What is physical abuse?

The Administration for Community Living defines physical abuse as inflicting physical pain or injury on a senior.[xxv]

What are examples of physical abuse?

- hitting
- slapping
- pinching
- forced feeding
- shoving
- grabbing
- shaking
- withholding food, water, medication, or medical care
- stealing medication
- using a weapon or throwing objects

What are tangible signs of physical abuse?

- cuts or punctures
- abrasions
- bruises
- sores
- internal bleeding
- swelling
- scars
- fractured or broken bones
- dislocations
- burns, scalds, and blisters
- missing teeth
- missing clumps of hair
- poor hygiene, including an unkempt appearance, unpleasant body odor, or dirty mouth
- unexplained weight loss
- loose-fitting clothes
- dentures that no longer fit
- lack of food in the refrigerator and cabinets
- wet or dried urine or feces in underclothes, the bed, or elsewhere in the home
- dehydration
- malnourishment
- filthy or insect/rodent-infested surroundings
- illness from medication being withheld

What are intangible signs of physical abuse?

Intangible and subtle signs of physical abuse are more difficult to detect because some injuries are not readily visible. Examples include:

- implausible or shifting explanations from either the caregiver or the elder about how an injury occurred
- feigned ignorance as to how an injury occurred
- frequent visits to the emergency room
- visits to different medical facilities to conceal frequency of injuries
- changes in the senior's demeanor such as becoming withdrawn, unsure, anxious, nervous, depressed, fearful, or submissive, especially around the caregiver
- poor eye contact
- insomnia or lethargy, perhaps from being overmedicated
- rubbing or favoring a part of the body in an attempt to soothe soreness
- rocking or humming to comfort oneself

What should I do if I suspect a caregiver of physical abuse?

There are several steps you can take. First, seek medical treatment for your relative if necessary. Document any injuries or suspicious behavior you observe, along with the dates and times of each occurrence. Include the location of the injury, distinguishing characteristics, such as size and color, and how the caregiver said the injury occurred. Take photos of the injury and notify local law enforcement and Adult Protective Services. Check the website of the National Adult Protective Services Association for your nearest agency or contact the elder abuse telephone hotline (see Resources).

The more cognitively impaired your parent is, the less likely they will be able to tell you they are being abused. You may want to consider installing a camera to monitor how your loved one's caregivers are treating them. Videos surface regularly in the news and on the internet depicting abuse by paid caregivers. I remember one video on the news that showed a caregiver punching and smacking her bedridden male client who suffered from Alzheimer's. The man's daughter worked so she hired someone to care for her father during the day. When the daughter returned home each evening, she would ask her father about his day. He always said everything had gone fine, but the daughter decided to install a surveillance camera just to be sure. The footage was heartbreaking. Her father's loss of short-term memory prevented him from recalling the physical abuse—an ability his caregiver recognized and easily exploited. Without the video, the daughter may have never discovered what was really happening to her father while she was at work and the abuse would have continued.

If you decide to install a surveillance camera, make sure that you understand the federal and state privacy and consent laws on this issue. Most states prohibit installing a hidden camera in places where persons captured on the tape would have a reasonable expectation of privacy, such as a bathroom. Audio recording without the consent of all parties to the conversation is illegal in some states but others have limited the protection to communications where the parties have a reasonable expectation of privacy.

Also, some families opt to install a camera in plain view, putting the caregiver on notice that their actions are being monitored. A surveillance camera could be a deal breaker for caregivers who view the presence of monitoring devices as an indication that the family does not trust them, but you have to do what you think is best. A non-abusive caregiver has nothing to hide.

What is emotional abuse?

The Centers for Disease Control and Prevention define emotional or psychological abuse of an elder as "verbal or nonverbal behaviors that inflict anguish, mental pain, fear, or distress on an older adult."[xxvi]

What are examples of emotional or verbal abuse?

Emotional abuse has very real consequences and can take a physical, as well as psychological, toll on its victims. Typical forms of emotional abuse include:

- yelling
- name-calling
- humiliating or insulting a person
- threatening to withhold food, medication, or to place the elder in a nursing home
- blocking contact with family and friends
- barring or limiting access to communication devices
- preventing the elder from leaving home
- withholding access to, and information about, the senior's finances, assets, and personal belongings
- destroying or refusing to give an elderly person their assistive devices, such as eyeglasses or a walker.

What are signs of emotional abuse?

Emotional abuse can be particularly difficult to detect because there are no visible scars, and abusers are careful to hide their behavior. Victims often suffer in silence because they are dependent on or fearful of their abuser. This is especially true for individuals with dementia and no immediate family or friends nearby to check on them. Signs of emotional abuse include:

- withdrawal from normal activities
- frequent unavailability or not feeling up to receiving company
- a change in personality or routine
- unusual fatigue or depression
- anxiety or fear of making the caregiver angry
- seeming intimidated or meek in the caregiver's presence
- an inability to have a private conversation outside of the caregiver's presence

What should I do if I suspect a caregiver of emotional abuse?

The type and severity of the abuse will determine whether you should terminate the caregiver, whether the problem stems from a lack of training, or whether the caregiver's conduct is subject to modification through counseling. For example, some people are just not aware of how their speaking style comes across to others. You have probably said to someone at one time or another, "Stop yelling at me," only to have the person reply, "I wasn't yelling." Also, caregivers from different countries or cultures may speak in a style that comes across as abrupt, loud, or disrespectful. If you are pleased with the other aspects of care your loved one is receiving, then you may want to speak to the caregiver about modifying their verbal delivery.

A lot of people would be surprised to learn that yelling, name-calling, insults, punishing, withholding, and threats constitute abuse—even when done for the senior's "own good." A part of you may even feel vindicated when you observe a caregiver treating your relative harshly because you understand the caregiver's frustration. You know from personal experience how stubborn and uncooperative your relative can be. But, here's the problem: emotional abuse can escalate to physical abuse. Therefore, do not allow caregivers to talk to your parent in anything but the most kind, patient, and firm manner. Because, the bottom line is, you are paying for good care, not attitude. You want caregivers who have the ability to remain calm and defuse situations by, for example, redirecting your parent's attention. A caregiver who has to yell and threaten to get a client to cooperate needs to find another field of work.

What is neglect?

According to the National Center on Elder Abuse, neglect is "the refusal or failure to fulfill any part of a person's obligations or duties of care to an elder which include, but are not limited to, life necessities such as food, water, clothing, shelter, personal hygiene, medicine, comfort and personal safety."[xxvii] A caregiver may neglect a person either by intentionally failing to perform their caregiving responsibilities or by unintentionally failing to provide proper care because of inadequate or improper training or other factors.

What are examples of neglect?

- failure to seek proper medical treatment for a vulnerable adult in a timely manner
- failure to follow the senior's prescribed plan of care
- isolation
- failure to refill medication
- failure to protect a senior from extreme temperatures and severe weather
- failure to maintain basic amenities such as a refrigerator, stove, running water, and a working toilet
- failure to provide nutritious and sufficient food and drink
- inadequate care resulting in preventable bedsores
- failure to keep the senior's person, clothing, and surroundings clean and insect-free
- failure to provide the senior with assistive devices
- leaving a vulnerable person unattended and without care and supervision for an extended period of time

What are signs of neglect?

Signs of neglect are often similar to signs of physical abuse, which are:

- poor hygiene, such as an unkempt appearance, unpleasant body odor, or dirty mouth
- unsuitable or inadequate clothing for the weather
- unusual weight loss

- dry skin or cracks around the corners of the mouth
- malnourishment
- dehydration
- diarrhea
- frequent infections
- sunken eyes
- empty refrigerator and cabinets
- filthy or insect/rodent-infested surroundings
- home in disrepair or that has fire and safety hazards
- hoarding conditions
- utilities turned off (no heat, electricity, water, gas, or cooling)
- a non-working toilet
- a lack of assistance with eating and drinking
- an absence of assistive devices the person needs
- absence of or insufficient medication

Self-neglect by seniors is another form of this issue and is more prevalent than neglect by others. Some elderly individuals are unable to cook for themselves, unable to remember to take their medication or to take the right dosage at the right time, and unable to keep themselves clean. Even if a person has a caregiver but does not have round-the-clock care, it is possible that the neglect you observe occurred while the caregiver was off duty. Also, sometimes symptoms could have a perfectly logical explanation that has nothing to do with abuse. Dehydration, for example, is a side effect of many medications. Do not immediately assume neglect but do not discount the possibility either.

What should I do if I suspect a caregiver of neglect?

If you suspect neglect, get medical attention for your parent. Also, if appropriate, contact the police and/or Adult Protective Services in your area.

What is financial abuse?

The Centers for Disease Control and Prevention define financial abuse as the "illegal, unauthorized, or improper use of an elder's money, benefits, belongings, property, or assets for the benefit of someone other than the older adult.[xxviii] This form of abuse is increasing at an alarming rate and perpetrators may use force, coercion, undue influence, or deception—such as identity theft—to get what they want. Pilfering an elder's property also falls into this category. A friend discovered that her mother's caregiver was stealing food, toilet tissue, paper towels, and aluminum foil. Anyone who shops for these items knows they are not inexpensive.

The more dependent a senior is on the caregiver, the more vulnerable the senior becomes and the more likely the senior is to acquiesce to the caregiver's requests for money, property, or favors—"I need new tires for my car or I won't be able to work for you anymore." I have also heard of cases where the elder goes along even when they know the caregiver is lying or using them. In cases like this, the senior is usually lonely and willing to pay for the caregiver's time and attention.

Financial abuse can have serious consequences for the elderly in particular. Victims often do not recoup their losses which leads to a decline in their standard of living. Financial abuse also results in shock at being betrayed, a loss of trust in others, and feelings of embarrassment and despair. One elderly victim of financial abuse in Virginia suffered a seizure at her bank upon learning that her account had been depleted. She had given her aide power of attorney without fully comprehending the possible consequences of her action.[xxix]

Sadly, financial abuse is underreported and can be difficult to prove. If a caregiver claims that money they received from their client was a gift, the elder may not refute it or, in some cases, may not even remember. I heard about one unscrupulous caregiver who took his client to see an attorney to draw up a will leaving everything to the caregiver. The client just happened to mention to his son that the caregiver had taken him "for a ride" and the father "signed some papers" while they were out. He did not recall the name or address of the office but remembered the general vicinity. The son drove his father around the area, and miraculously, the father spotted the attorney's office. The son was able to get the will voided, but what a close call!

What are examples of financial abuse?

- stealing
- forging signatures on checks, loan applications, or other documents
- using ATM or credit cards without permission
- misdirecting funds to unauthorized accounts
- persuading a mentally impaired senior to change the beneficiaries of their will or life insurance policy
- overcharging for caregiver services
- stealing someone's identity
- borrowing money or property and not paying the money back or returning the property

What are signs of financial abuse?

According to the American Bankers Association, "the key to spotting financial abuse is a change in a person's established financial patterns."[xxx] Common signs of financial exploitation include:

- uncharacteristically making frequent trips to the bank or using ATM machines
- increased credit card activity
- changes in the senior's lifestyle or spending habits
- unexplained addition of a new name to the senior's financial accounts

- signing over a deed or power of attorney to an unlikely individual, such as a caregiver
- incurring penalties by early withdrawal of funds or liquidating financial products, such as CDs, before maturity
- closing out long-held bank accounts
- checks that do not match the senior's known signature
- missing checks or checks written out of order
- bills or charges for items the elder cannot use or does not need
- unexplained withdrawals of large sums of money
- the elder is accompanied to the bank by someone who stands close by or even takes the cash out of the senior's hands and is not known to bank personnel
- implausible explanations by the senior or caregiver for bank transactions
- investing in risky financial products or business deals
- unexplained grocery receipts for food items that the senior does not eat; larger quantities than the senior can consume; or odd purchases such as dog food when the senior has no pets
- the elder begins to doubt their own ability to make sound financial decisions despite being capable
- unpaid and overdue bills
- bounced checks
- a change in the senior's financial circumstances
- unfamiliar entries on the senior's credit report
- a lack of basic supplies and goods which the senior can easily afford
- unexplained disappearance of valuables
- intentional isolation of elder from friends and family
- the caregiver and elder acting in a secretive manner
- the caregiver becomes the senior's new "best friend"

- donations to unfamiliar charities
- using different bank branches where staff is not familiar with the senior's banking habits
- alleged gifts of money, property, or valuables to caregiver
- charges to '800' numbers and risky online activities such as gambling
- mail is rerouted without knowledge and/or permission
- the caregiver always wants to get the mail first
- changes to a will or trust which benefit the caregiver
- new or changes to existing power of attorney
- relatives and friends of the caregiver added to the elder's payroll

What should I do if I suspect the caregiver of financial abuse?

Report your suspicions or proof of financial abuse to the police so they can investigate. Write down what you observe and make copies of corroborating documents. Notify your parent's bank, if appropriate, and enlist their help. If checks are stolen, contact your relative's financial institution immediately and request a stop payment on the stolen checks. It may be necessary to close the account altogether. In the case of identity theft or fraud, visit www.identitytheft.gov regarding steps you can take. Contact all three credit bureaus—TransUnion, Experian, and Equifax—and put a fraud alert on your parent's credit report. Also, ask Adult Protective Services in your area for assistance. Keep in mind that individuals with dementia sometimes misplace or hide items.

What is sexual abuse?

The National Center on Elder Abuse defines sexual abuse as "non-consensual sexual contact of any kind with an older adult, perpetrated through force, threats, or the exploitation of authority."[xxxi]

What are examples of sexual abuse of the elderly?

- rape
- sodomy
- nonconsensual touching
- forcing the senior to undress
- forcing the senior to take sexually explicit photographs
- forcing the senior to watch pornography

What are signs of sexual abuse?

- bruises or redness near the breasts, anus, or genital area
- unexplained sexually transmitted diseases
- pain, soreness, or bleeding in the genital or anal area
- difficulty walking or sitting
- behavioral signs of distress such as being anxious or withdrawn
- bloody or torn underclothes

What should I do if I suspect a caregiver of sexual abuse?

Make sure that your parent receives medical treatment and seek assistance from Adult Protective Services for additional support and guidance. If the claim is substantiated or if other issues arise, APS will work with your parent and family members to address the problem and find ways to prevent any reoccurrence. Be aware that the agency will defer to your relative's wishes if they are mentally competent. This means that your parent has the right to refuse any assistance from APS. For persons who are not mentally competent, the agency will do what is necessary to protect them, including removal from the home. If a crime has been committed, the agency will contact the police if you have not already done so.

How can I prevent my relative from being abused?

- The best way to prevent or minimize the likelihood of abuse by caregivers is to carefully screen workers before you hire them. Agencies claim, and many people assume, that caregivers hired through agencies have undergone a thorough background check. But a 2012 study by Northwestern University of one hundred and eighty for-profit home care agencies located in several different states, found that only fifty-five percent of agencies conducted a federal criminal background check, and only one-third reported performing drug tests before hiring caregivers.[xxxii] So, regardless of an agency's assurances, you should perform your own background check. If, for some reason, you are unable to perform a background check before the caregiver begins work, do so as soon as possible. Read more about background checks in chapter two, entitled ISO The Ideal Caregiver.
- Family members should maintain a regular presence in the elderly person's life not only to provide support, but also to observe what is going on. People are most vulnerable when they are left alone. Ask friends to drop by unannounced to see how the caregiver is treating your parent. You want to have as many eyes and ears monitoring the situation as possible, especially if you are managing your relative's care from a distance.

  If you haven't told your parent's neighbors that your parent now has a caregiver, they have probably figured it out. A person who shows up on a regular basis wearing scrubs is a big clue. Nevertheless, give a couple of neighbors your telephone number and the caregiver's schedule and ask them to call if they notice people visiting the caregiver during work hours, if the caregiver arrives late or leaves early, or if they spot any other unusual activity. There may be a perfectly logical explanation for non-routine activity, but it is better to be on the safe side. Many seniors' neighbors have moved closer to their adult children, moved into a facility, passed away, or grown frail, and are now in need of assistance themselves. Hopefully, your parent is fortunate enough to have neighbors willing to get involved.

The more physically or cognitively impaired your parent is, the more family and friends need to be involved in making sure that they are receiving proper care and not being abused. Elders are often reluctant to report abuse because they are embarrassed, afraid of the perpetrator, or afraid of being removed from their home and placed in a facility. If your relative has full-blown dementia, the caregiver may try to cast doubt on their veracity.

- It is essential to convey to the caregiver that your relative is loved and respected. In other words, do not let illness define your parent. Make sure their caregiver knows about your parent's career, hobbies, artistic talents, and military and community service. Perhaps your parent taught school, lived abroad for several years, knitted the throw on the chair in the bedroom, led a Boy Scout troop, grew up on a farm, or played a musical instrument. Place photographs around the home showing your relative living a happy and vibrant life, surrounded by people who love them. Without a fuller picture of your parent's life, it is easy for a caregiver to see their job as nothing more than a series of thankless tasks being performed for a stranger—a stranger who may be distant and uncommunicative.
- Beware of a caregiver who encourages family members to leave as soon as they arrive for work. The aide may try to convince you that it is important for your relative to get used to them, but ignore this request. One of my mother's caregivers quit one week after she started work, claiming that I did not trust her. Her evidence was that I stayed a while after she arrived. A good caregiver would have known that dashing out and leaving my mother with a stranger would have made my mother anxious. There needs to be an adjustment or

transition period. Second, a good caregiver would have appreciated that I stayed in case they had questions. For the caregiver to assume that my remaining an hour or so after she showed up was somehow about her was troubling. I was spending time with my mother, not working a job. When the caregiver said she was not coming back, I did not try to dissuade her. And the fact that she did not discuss her concerns with me before quitting spoke volumes.

- Examine your relative's body routinely to check for signs of physical abuse or unusual changes. Helping them bathe or get ready for bed are ideal opportunities.
- If possible, have your parent participate in activities outside of the home. Isolated elders are more attractive targets than people who engage with their surrounding community. Also, make sure that your parent sees their doctors, dentist, therapists, podiatrist, and other health care professionals on a regular basis. Not only for the purpose of maintaining their health, but because these professionals are familiar with signs of elder abuse and will know how to respond.
- Consider installing a surveillance camera, especially if you are trying to monitor your relative's care long-distance. Each state has laws governing the use of surveillance cameras, so make sure that you are in compliance.
- The first step in safeguarding your relative's financial information is to keep checks, credit cards, financial statements, and other personal documents in a secure location or locked file cabinet that only your relative or a trusted individual can access. Note the expiration date on all credit cards in case a replacement card does not arrive.
- Seniors are often targeted in identity theft scams. Stealing the identity of a senior with good credit permits the perpetrator to obtain credit cards, loans, and utility accounts, such as gas and electricity, in the senior's name. You should report unauthorized financial activity as soon as possible. Sometimes, reporting unauthorized charges is time-sensitive.

You don't want to discover two years later that a caregiver was paying their bills with money from your loved one's account and then try to recover the money from the bank. The first question the bank representative will ask is why it took you so long to let them know.

- Reconcile bank statements as soon as they become available or monitor account transactions online regularly to see if unauthorized activity has occurred. Many people assume that banks program their computers to flag unusual or suspicious account activity. However, not every bank has automated its monitoring processes. The deceitful caregiver mentioned at the beginning of this chapter stole a lot of her elderly victim's money by withdrawing four hundred dollars a day over the course of two years without detection. The lesson here is that you cannot depend on someone else to monitor and protect your parent's assets.
- Shred bank statements, cancelled checks, and other financial documents, or discontinue paper statements altogether and access account information online. Reducing the amount of confidential information that is mailed to your parent's home decreases the opportunities for financial abuse.
- Run a credit check at least once a year to see if your relative has fallen victim to identity theft. People can open accounts in someone else's name and arrange to have statements sent to a different address, a PO box, or pay bills online. Fraud can go undetected for years if people fail to monitor their accounts. Visit the Federal Trade Commission's website (see Resources) to learn how to obtain a free report from the three major credit bureaus.
- If your relative does not need to apply for credit soon, consider putting a credit or security freeze on their credit file. A freeze will prevent new creditors from accessing your parent's credit report, thereby blocking identity thieves from opening new accounts in your loved one's name. The freeze can be lifted at any time. Fees are nominal and vary from state

to state. To effectively restrict access, you must contact all three main credit bureaus.

- If your relative does not receive a statement from their bank or credit card company, act immediately. Someone may have intentionally diverted the statement to prevent your relative from discovering unauthorized charges.
- Prevent checks from being intercepted by arranging for direct deposit of as much income as possible, including Social Security checks, pension payments, dividends, and income tax refunds. Also, set up automatic bill pay to reduce the need for checks or cash.
- Ask if your parent's bank will alert a designated family member if they spot possible fraudulent account activity. Some banks still see such action as a violation of a customer's right to privacy, but others will cooperate if they have the account holder's permission or if bank staff know the family member.
- Consider using a service to monitor your parent's credit card accounts for suspicious or unusual activity.
- Review receipts to ensure that only items for your relative's use were purchased. An exception would be where the caregiver is a live-in, which is discussed in more detail later in the book. The rule for live-ins is they eat the food and use the household products provided by the client. In the event the live-in wants something different, they pay for it. If you notice an unusual item, speak up. Not in an accusatory tone, but diplomatically. It is natural to let one or two things slide, especially when the caregiver is working out well on other fronts. But the caregiver may construe the family's failure to speak up as a sign that the family is inattentive, complacent, or afraid to upset the status quo. This is not healthy because it gives the caregiver the upper hand. You should always treat employees in a respectful and courteous manner, but do not become passive.

- If you are providing the caregiver with a car to transport your relative, check the odometer occasionally to see if the caregiver is driving more than they claim.
- Set up a trusted family member with view-only online access to your parent's accounts. An individual may become too mentally incapacitated to understand their finances, and preventative measures can help safeguard their savings and financial independence.
- If you discover your parent's caregiver is sharing their personal financial woes with your relative, tell the caregiver to cease immediately. If the caregiver continues to bring up the subject, seriously consider replacing them. Their comments may be a thinly veiled attempt to win sympathy and, ultimately, obtain financial assistance from your parent.
- If your parent's pain medicine no longer seems to be effective, it could be that their caregiver is stealing medication. Healthcare professionals struggle with addiction just like workers in any other profession. It is not unusual for caregivers to lose their license because of stealing their patients' drugs. It is also not that difficult to do, especially if a client is mentally impaired and there is minimal or no oversight. Some caregivers go so far as to switch pills to cover their tracks.
- If the caregiver must shop for your parent, provide them with a prepaid debit card with sufficient funds to cover your relative's monthly expenses and just add funds to the card as needed. This method limits your relative's financial exposure.
- Warn your loved one not to sign any legal documents—especially a Power of Attorney—unless someone knowledgeable and trustworthy has reviewed them.
- Review Medicare statements as soon as you receive them. You may uncover nothing more sinister than an inadvertent error or you may find that someone else is using your relative's benefits. If you suspect your relative has been the victim of Medicare fraud, contact the U.S. Centers for

Medicare and Medicaid Services (see Resources). Be prepared to provide your parent's name and Medicare number and to explain why a particular claim is fraudulent. Depending on the nature of the fraud, you may also have to include the name of the service provider and the date the services, supplies, or equipment were allegedly delivered.

- Photograph or video valuable or irreplaceable objects in the home. If possible, move these items to a separate room that others have no legitimate need to enter or place smaller items in a safe deposit box. I know of a case where the caregiver replaced her elderly client's silver dollars with fifty-cent pieces.
- Through services such as OptOutPrescreen, you can prevent creditors and insurers from sending your parent unsolicited firm offers of credit and insurance. People can opt out for five years via the company website and opt out permanently by mail (see Resources). Opting back in can be done at any time.
- Reduce the amount of junk mail your relative receives by registering with the Data and Marketing Association's DMAchoice service (see Resources).
- On the USPS website (see Resources), sign your parent up for Informed Delivery, a free service which emails eligible customers digital images of letters and packages scheduled for delivery. The majority of addresses in the United States are eligible for the service but some are not. An example would be apartment complexes where the street address and zip code are the same for all residents even though they have individual mailboxes. Addresses must be unique to ensure that people don't receive images of someone else's mail. This feature is especially useful for the family of an elderly person because they can see what mail is supposed to be coming to their parent's home and if the mail is being intercepted.
- If possible, do not leave outgoing mail containing personal information to be picked up by the letter carrier. Give outgoing mail directly to the letter carrier or put mail in a USPS mailbox.

- Monitor telephone and cable bills to see if anyone has upgraded to expensive cable services that were not authorized.
- Sign your loved one up for the do-not-call registry to reduce the number of unwanted solicitations from legitimate companies. You can register for free at www.donotcall.gov, a service administered by the Federal Trade Commission (see Resources). Non-profit organizations, political organizations, debtors, and groups taking surveys are exempt from the registry. Residents of Pennsylvania and Wyoming can get on a do-not-call list through DMAchoice (see Resources).
- Consider instructing your relative's financial institution not to cash personal checks above a certain amount without verbal authorization from your parent or another authorized person. I put this procedure in place with my mother's bank in case one of her checks or her account numbers fell into the wrong hands. I set a dollar amount high enough to cover all of the bills. The bank put an alert on my mother's account, instructing any teller presented with a check above the specified amount to contact me for verification before cashing the check. This only works if the payee presents the check directly to the payer's bank. If presented to a different bank or a check cashing store, for example, the alert is not triggered.
- Maintain professional boundaries. It is easy for caregivers to become close to their clients and the clients' family because of the nature of the work and because of the amount of time they all spend together. There is nothing improper if a friendship develops as long as professional boundaries are maintained. Failure to do so can cause caregivers to take your relative for granted and take inappropriate liberties.
- Trust, but verify. Former President Ronald Reagan famously said these words regarding U.S. arms control negotiations with Russia, but it applies to many other situations, too. You should assume that your relative's caregivers are honest and professional. That's the "trust" part. Yet, remain vigilant and

make it a point to double-check regularly that your parent is receiving the best care possible.

- If one family member handles your relative's finances, another trustworthy member should have read-only online access to the accounts. This is not a reflection on anyone's character. It's just another example of "trust, but verify." Having a back-up person also means that someone can step in and be up to speed if, for some reason, the primary person can no longer serve in the role.
- Trust your instincts. Sometimes a caregiver seems great, but something about the person bothers you. You can't put your finger on the concern so you tell yourself that it must be your imagination and tamp down your suspicions. Don't. The stakes are too high. In most instances, if you think about it for a while, you will be able to identify what makes you uncomfortable about that person.

Federal and state governments have lagged in their response to elder abuse. Program funding is limited and there is a lack of uniformity in the reporting of abuse. The good news, however, is that legislatures are beginning to take more decisive action to assist and protect seniors.

Several states have made financial professionals, such as investment advisors, mandatory reporters of suspected financial abuse of the elderly or other vulnerable adults. Many of these states also give financial advisors discretion not to disburse client funds for a set period of time while their reservations are investigated. This is a powerful tool because, too often, money lost as a result of financial exploitation is never recovered.

Some states have enacted legislation similar to slayer statutes that prevent a person's killer from inheriting from the victim. Laws in Arizona, California, Illinois, Kentucky, Maryland, Michigan, Oregon, and Washington now prohibit an elderly or dependent person's abuser from inheriting as well. The specifics vary among the states, such as the forms of abuse covered, the nature of the relationship between the abuser and the victim, and if a criminal conviction is required. For example, a finding of abuse by clear and convincing evidence in civil court triggers the disinheritance provision in California. However, the abuser is not disqualified from inheriting if the victim "was substantially able to manage his or her financial resources and to resist fraud or undue influence" after the alleged abuse occurred. In other words, the state legislature took into account that some people may forgive their abuser and still want to remember the person in their will.

California, Illinois, Nevada, and Maine have passed laws that presume undue influence when caregivers receive property or money from an elderly person upon death. These statutes void testamentary gifts and shift the burden of proof to the recipient to prove that undue influence was not a factor. Examples of differences among the statutes include if family members are included, if the caregiver earned wages, and if a threshold dollar amount is required to trigger the presumption. These laws are intended to reduce financial elder abuse by removing the profit motive. Shifting the burden of proof also gives families contesting such gifts a stronger case. However, in some states' zeal to address this growing problem, these laws have had unexpected consequences. Sometimes, an elderly person really *did* intend to leave a gift to a dedicated and valued caregiver, but the caregiver is unable to overcome the presumption of undue influence. Some states such as California and Nevada exclude gifts from the presumption if the document transferring the gift from the elder to the caregiver was reviewed by an independent attorney and satisfied other criteria set forth in the statute.

Some shrewd caregivers have tried to circumvent these legal protections by marrying the elderly person because, historically, spouses have not had to overcome a presumption of undue influence. California has responded to this latest maneuver by extending the presumption of undue influence to gifts made to spouses who were the caregiver of a dependent adult if the gifts were made during the marriage or within ninety days after the caregiver's services were last provided, and the elderly person died less than six months after the marriage commenced. Elder law is complex and specific to each state, and the information provided in this book is not meant to provide legal advice. Families should consult a licensed attorney specializing in elder or probate law to protect their loved one and their assets.

I found out that my parent's caregiver had another day job and took my parent to work with them. I really like the caregiver but feel they were dishonest. Should I fire them?

A former coworker of mine discovered that her mother's caregiver was driving her mother to the caregiver's other day job. The caregiver told the family that she took their mother—who had dementia—out during the day so that their mother could "get some fresh air." The family was delighted until their mother began talking about a house and a man that she visited regularly. At first, the daughters thought their mother was confused because of her illness, but she seemed so certain. When the family questioned the caregiver, she admitted that she had another job with conflicting hours. The caregiver was adamant that their mother was never in any danger. In fact, the caregiver said that her two clients spent the time chatting and enjoying each other's company. In the end, the daughters told the caregiver that they disapproved of her deception, but they did not fire her. She continued working her other job with their permission. The family was satisfied with the care their mother was receiving overall and was sensitive to the fact that the caregiver needed to make more money. Don't judge until you discover how hard it is to find good caregivers.

CHAPTER 6

$TICKER $HOCK: THE COST OF LONG-TERM CARE

In the early 1900s, Auguste Deter became the first person to be diagnosed with presenile dementia, now known as Alzheimer's disease. The cost of her care was expensive for the times, and Auguste's husband tried to have her moved to a cheaper asylum.

Unfortunately, not much has changed. In the United States, long-term care costs have steadily risen and will continue to do so. Cost increases are mainly the result of three factors: high demand due to the large number of aging baby boomers and their parents, the critical shortage of caregivers, and the extension of federal minimum wage and overtime protection laws to most caregivers.

What can I expect to pay for in-home care?

Caregiver rates depend on several factors, including location. Rates are highest in populous states such as New York and California because there is a greater demand for services and in less inhabited states such as Alaska and North Dakota because available workers are in short supply. Southern states have the lowest caregiver rates.

The cost of in-home care also depends on the level of care required. Caregivers who assist high-needs clients command a higher rate, while those who primarily provide companionship usually charge a lot less. According to the 2021 Cost of Care Survey by Genworth, the median hourly rate for homemaker services, such as cleaning and cooking, was $26.00, and $27.00 for personal care services such as bathing and dressing.[xxxiii] This means that half of the caregivers in the survey earned more than the median rate and half earned less. Participants included homecare agencies and facilities such as nursing homes, but not private duty workers. Caregivers also factor in their experience and training to establish their rate. Some aides are certified nursing assistants (CNAs) with extensive experience while others are new and trying to break into the field.

Live-in caregivers usually charge a flat daily rate, which can vary depending on whether the aide has their own home or lives with the client. Lodging, meals, and access to a vehicle for personal use can offset some of the cost. Rates for live-in caregivers range anywhere from about $1,000 to $5,000 per month.

Initially, I paid the aide who cared for my mother during the day a higher hourly rate than the caregiver who provided companionship at night. The caregiver who worked during the day helped my mother shower and get dressed, prepared her meals, and made her bed. After my mother's second stroke, however, everyone I hired directly received the same rate because she needed the same level of care constantly.

Will I save money by hiring a caregiver directly?

Hiring caregivers privately cost me twenty to fifty percent less than hiring through an agency. However, remember that your goal is to get the best affordable care you can for your parent and not necessarily the cheapest. Caregivers who agree to a low rate may quit when a better paying job comes along, and their departure could come at a most inopportune time for you. Workers who feel taken advantage of—even if they agree to your terms initially—may not give their best. Also, be wary of rates that seem too good to be true, such as caring for a high-needs client for minimum wage. Caregivers may hope that a low wage will prevent you from delving too deeply into their background. CNAs who have lost their license for committing abuse, neglect, or fraud at a nursing home often look for work in a private home setting.

If you decide to use an agency, I recommend getting quotes from at least three companies. I found a difference of more than five dollars per hour among the agencies I used. Over the course of a forty-hour workweek, that difference adds up to $10,400 a year, which is a considerable amount for most families

If I use an agency, do I have to agree to a minimum number of hours per day?

Many agencies require a minimum number of hours that their aides must work because it is difficult to find caregivers willing to work only a couple hours a day. A lot of caregivers hold out for an assignment with longer hours so they can make more money. If your relative requires fewer than three hours per day, you will have more success hiring a caregiver on your own than going through an agency.

The agency I want to use said they require a deposit upfront. Is this standard practice?

Be wary of agencies that require an upfront deposit before any services have been rendered. The agency could have its license revoked or go out of business. Moreover, disputing an invoice is more difficult when the agency already has your money.

If I hire a caregiver directly, what are my financial obligations other than payroll?

As an employer, you are responsible for withholding federal income taxes if the employee asks. State income tax withholding laws vary and you can contact your comptroller's office to learn what your obligations are.

As of 2022, employers must also withhold Social Security and Medicare taxes for any household employee paid at least $2,400 during the year. The current rates are 6.2 percent and 1.45 percent, respectively. These taxes are authorized by the Federal Insurance Contributions Act or FICA. Also, employers must match the FICA taxes they withhold for each employee. This money comes out of the employers' pocket and they are prohibited from taking their share out of their employees' check.

In some instances, employers have to pay federal unemployment taxes, or FUTA. IRS Publication 926, entitled "Household Employer's Tax Guide," is a must-read for anyone employing domestic workers. Depending on the state, unemployment insurance taxes may apply.

Several states require employers to carry workers' compensation insurance that allows injured employees to receive benefits regardless of fault or negligence on the part of the employer. If an aide sustains a work-related injury, the costs could be considerable, and if you do not have this insurance, you could be held personally liable for medical expenses, lost wages, and job retraining. I was able to obtain a workers' compensation rider on my mother's homeowners insurance policy. The premiums were based on her caregivers' projected wages for a year. At the end of that period, the insurance company audited the payroll records to ensure that the premiums they charged were commensurate with the company's exposure in the event of a future claim. The company ultimately determined that the actual payroll exceeded the estimated amount and my mother had to pay a premium adjustment, which turned out to be negligible. You do not want to be caught off guard if a worker submits a claim and you have not been paying into the fund. Consult your appropriate state agency to determine if you are required to carry either or both workers' compensation and state unemployment insurance.

Also, currently, California, Hawaii, New Jersey, New York, and Rhode Island require employers to offer disability benefits to employees who become unable to work because of injury or illness. This short-term, temporary financial assistance pays a portion of the disabled employees' salary. Unlike workers' compensation insurance, disability insurance covers non-work-related injury or illness.

Am I required to pay caregivers at least the federal minimum wage?

There is a lot of confusion about this issue because for decades, federal minimum wage laws did not apply to domestic workers such as caregivers. As of January 1, 2015, however, most caregivers are entitled to minimum wage protection. The exceptions are workers who primarily provide companionship, as long as they are hired directly by the family. The companionship exemption does not apply to third parties, such as caregiver agencies. Agencies must pay caregivers at least the federal minimum wage regardless of the type of services provided. Also, despite the federal exemption, some states have passed laws providing minimum wage protection for companion caregivers.

In order to qualify for the companion services exemption and avoid paying federal minimum wage, the following criteria must be met:

- the caregiver cannot spend more than twenty percent of the total weekly hours worked assisting with ADLs or IADLs
- the caregiver cannot perform medically-related services that require or are routinely performed by trained personnel, such as registered nurses or CNAs
- the caregiver may not perform any domestic service, such as cooking or doing laundry, for other members of the household.

During any week that these criteria are not met, the family cannot claim the federal companionship exemption and must pay minimum wage for *all* hours worked during that week.

To further complicate matters, under certain circumstances, a caregiver can be employed by both the family and an agency or other third party. This arrangement is known as joint employment and can make the family liable for paying minimum wage if the third-party employer does not. In determining if joint employment exists, a court would review the entire employment situation, including the following guidance criteria published by the Department of Labor. Specifically, the issue depends on whether the family:

- hires or fires the caregiver
- supervises and controls the caregiver's work schedule or conditions of employment to a substantial degree
- determines the employee's rate of pay and method of payment
- maintains the employee's employment records

What is my obligation as an employer if the state and federal minimum wage rates differ?

Over half of the states, the District of Columbia, and some counties and cities have set a minimum wage rate higher than the federal government's. Employers must pay whichever wage rate is highest among the varying jurisdictions. Check the laws in your state, county, and city to determine the minimum wage rate that you have to pay.

Do I have to pay caregivers overtime?

Effective January 1, 2015, all home care workers are entitled to overtime pay under federal law with two main exceptions—caregivers who provide companionship, and live-in caregivers—but only if these workers are employed by the client or the client's family. Agencies or other third parties cannot claim the exemption and must pay their caregivers overtime. Also, during any week that the requirements for the companion exemption are not met, even caregivers employed by the family must receive overtime for all applicable hours.

As mentioned, live-in caregivers are generally exempt from the federal overtime requirement, but there are some exceptions. For example, an aide hired to help someone for a couple of weeks upon their discharge from the hospital would not qualify for the exemption. Neither would a live-in caregiver who works a twenty-four-hour shift but does not reside in the client's home on a permanent basis or for an extended period of time. Workers in both cases would be eligible for overtime pay. Finally, families may still be obligated to pay overtime under state law. Your state department of labor can advise you on this matter.

The same joint employment rules apply to overtime. If a third party, such as an agency, is a co-employer of the caregiver and fails to pay them overtime, the family could be held responsible.

Are family members providing care for their relative eligible for minimum wage and overtime pay?

If a family member is hired as a caregiver for your parent, then the same Fair Labor Standards Act (FLSA) protections and exemptions apply to them. Also, you do not have to compensate family members for services they would have normally performed due to their familial relationship. To avoid confusion, create a written care plan detailing the services the paid family member will provide. Some Medicaid-funded and some publicly funded agencies have to approve this type of plan before a family member can be hired to provide caregiver services. The U.S. Department of Labor's "Fact Sheet #79F" is available on the agency's website and provides more information on this topic along with examples.

What is the overtime pay rate?

The federal overtime rate is one and a half times a worker's regular pay rate for all hours worked above forty in a single workweek. The Wage and Hour Division of the U.S. Department of Labor publishes a helpful and easy-to-read booklet entitled "Paying Minimum Wage and Overtime to Home Care Workers" to help employers know and comply with labor laws. Most states adhere to the federal threshold of forty hours per week to determine overtime. Your state's employment services agency will be able to provide you with specific information on your obligation regarding overtime.

Do I have to pay overtime for holidays?

The federal government does not require employers to pay overtime for holidays but many agencies charge clients for overtime. Be sure that companies obtain your consent beforehand. The agencies I used charged overtime for Easter, Memorial Day, the Fourth of July, Labor Day, Thanksgiving, Christmas, and New Year's Eve. One agency charged overtime for Mother's Day.

When you hire caregivers directly, paying overtime for holidays depends on the arrangement you and the caregiver work out. The extra pay, however, will earn you a lot of goodwill and there will be times when you will need a favor from your caregiver.

If a caregiver works more than forty hours one week and fewer than forty hours the next week, may I reduce the amount of overtime pay owed by using the *average* number of hours worked each week?

You may not avoid paying overtime by averaging hours worked over more than one workweek. The way to manage overtime expenses is either to reduce the number of coverage hours or use multiple caregivers—which entails more scheduling and supervision— so that no one person works more than forty hours per week. No one disagrees that caregivers should be paid well for the hard work they do, but many families already struggle to handle this expense. Caregiver agencies fought vigorously against minimum wage and overtime protections for in-home healthcare workers by arguing that families would cut back on hours which, in turn, would jeopardize their loved one's care. The federal government, however, decided that these protections were long overdue for this group of workers.

Do I have to pay a live-in caregiver for the hours when they are asleep?

Under federal law, you do not have to pay a live-in caregiver for hours spent sleeping or engaging in other activities of a personal nature as long as you have a reasonable agreement in place that specifically excludes these time periods. The federal government does not require that agreements excluding sleep time from compensation be in writing, but memorializing these terms in a written agreement will prevent misunderstandings in the future.

However, states have their own labor laws and you should check with your labor department to find out if caregivers in your jurisdiction have to be paid for hours spent sleeping. The rationale for this policy is that workers who are on the premises are available to work. Some states also require that employers keep sleep logs as proof that a caregiver was not working during the sleep period set forth in the agreement. Either the client or the caregiver can maintain the sleep log.

Is there a minimum number of hours that live-in caregivers must be allowed to sleep?

Under federal law, live-in caregivers and those who work more than twenty-four hours in a shift must get an uninterrupted sleep period of at least five hours. Also, the sleep period must be scheduled. Caregivers cannot be required to get their rest in a catch-as-catch-can manner. State laws may vary.

If a caregiver is not a live-in, do I have to pay for time spent sleeping?

If the caregiver works fewer than twenty-four hours in one shift, then you must pay for the time spent sleeping. If the caregiver works a shift of twenty-four hours or more, you may exclude sleep hours if both parties agree, the caregiver's sleep is uninterrupted, and the employer provides adequate sleeping accommodations.

What is the maximum number of sleep hours that an employer can exclude?

Generally, the maximum number of excludable sleep hours is eight as long as the caregiver is paid for other hours worked within a prescribed period. The U.S. Department of Labor's "Fact Sheet #79D" is very helpful on this topic and is available on the agency's website.

Do I have to pay the caregiver if their sleep is interrupted by work?

If the caregiver's sleep is interrupted because of work, they must be compensated. And if the caregiver's sleep is interrupted in a way that prevents them from getting at least five consecutive hours of sleep during the agreed-upon period, then you may not exclude any sleep hours and must pay the caregiver for the entire sleep period.

Do I have to pay a live-in caregiver for personal time taken?

Employers do not have to compensate caregivers for personal time as long as the employee is not on duty at all and the amount of downtime is long enough for the caregiver to spend in a meaningful way—such as running errands.

Do I have to pay the live-in caregiver if their personal time is interrupted?

If the caregiver has to stop eating or otherwise interrupt their personal time to do any tasks for your parent, then they have to be compensated for the hours worked.

How often do I have to pay my parent's caregivers?

If you use caregiver agencies, the companies will stipulate the frequency of pay. If you hire a caregiver directly, you can negotiate this term as long as you comply with applicable state law.

Am I required to provide paid leave as a benefit?

The federal government does not require employers to provide paid leave for employees; however, several states have paid-leave laws. Usually, employees have to work a certain length of time before they can use their accrued leave. Contact the state employment agency responsible for enforcing labor laws in your jurisdiction to find out what your obligations are, if any, and if in-home personal care assistants are exempt. Also, consider providing leave as a benefit because unforeseen events come up in everyone's life. If your caregivers are employed by an agency, then it is the agency's responsibility to provide paid benefits, including leave.

Do I have to reimburse caregivers for mileage?

Out of fairness, you should reimburse caregivers who use their own vehicle to transport your relative, but you are not legally required to do so under federal law. State laws vary. Having said that, you will probably not keep caregivers very long if the cost of gas comes out of their paycheck. Each year the IRS sets a mileage reimbursement rate for federal employees who use their own vehicle for business. While you are not required to apply this rate if you reimburse your parent's workers for mileage, you may find this information useful. As of January 1, 2021, federal workers are allowed to deduct fifty-six cents per mile for business travel. You may also want to assist with the cost of public transportation to get back and forth to work, especially if your loved one lives far from the caregiver.

Please note that the Fact Sheets published by the U.S. Department of Labor are not law and are only intended for clarification.

CHAPTER 7

PAYING FOR IN-HOME CARE

Decades ago, the elderly depended on family members to care for them in their old age. But the supply of available family caregivers relative to the demand has fallen drastically, making the family care plan less viable. In 2010, there were more than seven potential family caregivers for every one person eighty years of age or older. By 2030, the ratio is projected to drop to four-to-one.[xxxiv] This critical demographic change is caused primarily by baby boomers having smaller families than their parents and grandparents. As a result, a higher percentage of elders who want to age in place will have to pay for in-home care.

A comprehensive analysis of long-term care funding options is beyond the scope of this book because both the public and private sectors are coming up with new plans at an unprecedented rate. However, this chapter will help you identify some of the major funding sources and understand the role of Medicaid and Medicare.

Does Medicare pay for in-home long-term care?

Medicare is the federal government's health insurance program and it covers workers once they reach sixty-five who paid into the system through payroll taxes. Younger individuals who qualify based on disability or disease are also covered. There is a lot of confusion about whether Medicare pays for long-term personal or custodial care in the home, and the short answer is no if that is the only kind of care the person needs. So many people mistakenly believe that they can rely on Medicare for their long-term care needs, that the Social Security Administration includes the following language in its annual benefits statement to workers: "Medicare does not pay for long-term care, so you may want to consider options for private insurance."

Medicare will pay for caregivers to assist with the activities of daily living (ADLs) for a short period of time if these services are provided in conjunction with skilled care such as nursing or therapy. The agency providing the healthcare workers must be Medicare-certified. Additional requirements include the person receiving assistance must be homebound and under the care of a doctor, and the services must be part of a plan of care established by their physician. Homebound does not mean bedridden. Rather, it means that it is difficult for the individual to leave home without an assistive device or help from another person. The Medicare recipient may leave home to attend activities such as adult day care, religious services, and funerals without jeopardizing their Medicare coverage.

Medicare does not typically cover meals delivered to the recipient's home or homemaking services, such as laundry and shopping for groceries. However, individuals receiving hospice care are eligible for personal care and homemaker services if they have a terminal illness and a life expectancy of six months or less.

Does Medicare Supplement Insurance (Medigap) cover long-term care?

Medigap insurance plans are designed to help pay out-of-pocket expenses for services covered by traditional Medicare Part A (hospital) and Part B (medical). These plans do not cover long-term care costs.

Do Medicare Advantage plans pay for long-term care?

Individuals with this type of plan receive traditional Medicare coverage through a private insurance company instead of through the federal government. To date, plans do not cover long-term in-home care.

Does Medicaid pay for personal care services in the home?

Medicaid is jointly funded by federal and state governments and provides health coverage—including assistance with ADLs and IADLs—to individuals who satisfy eligibility requirements. Each state administers its own program. Medicaid accounts for almost one-half of long-term care spending in the United States but, to qualify for coverage, individuals must be medically eligible, low-income with few assets, at least sixty-five years old, or physically or mentally disabled at any age. Although Medicaid is need-based, a high income is not an automatic bar to qualifying. The government takes many factors into account. High medical expenses, for example, might reduce someone's income enough to qualify.

In the past, Medicaid recipients had to be in a nursing home to receive long-term care services. But states now recognize that in-home care is more cost effective. Eligibility rules and requirements vary among the programs and programs differ across state lines. State income eligibility requirements may not be the same as federal guidelines. Some states limit their programs for home-based care to individuals with specific medical conditions or to certain geographical areas based on need and availability of managed care providers. Funding is limited and many states have a long waiting list; however, don't be deterred if this is something that could work for your parent. Some coverage groups have priority over others, depending on the program, and individuals in these groups sometimes move to the top of the list. Contact the agency that administers the Medicaid waiver program in your parent's state about the availability of in-home services.

Because state regulations differ, if your relative is already receiving long-term care at home under Medicaid and is contemplating a move to another state, be sure to research if your relative will still qualify for coverage at the same or a higher level.

Can people meet Medicaid asset requirements by giving assets away?

Currently, all states except California will assume that any gifts or transfers of assets made within five years of the date of your relative's Medicaid application, also known as the look-back period, were made for the express purpose of qualifying for Medicaid. California uses a shorter look-back period of thirty months. Reducing one's assets in violation of Medicaid rules can cause a delay in benefits—known as the penalty period. Therefore, you should check with your state to see what the current rules are. California plans to substantially increase its asset threshold and New York has announced that it will impose a look-back period—albeit a shorter term—for in-home care. In the past, the state's look-back period only applied to nursing home care. Also, there are several exceptions and exemptions that allow transfers during the look-back period without being penalized. A Medicaid expert can help you navigate these complex issues.

Do individuals have any recourse if their income exceeds the Medicaid threshold?

Each state sets its own "maximum allowable income" limit for Medicaid eligibility. Most states have medically needy or share-of-cost programs, which allow individuals whose income is too high to spend down the excess on qualifying medical care, and, thereby, satisfy the income requirements. Examples of qualifying expenses include: hospital and medical bills, prescription drugs, medical equipment, and assistive devices. States get to decide whether to offer the medically needy program to everyone who is eligible for Medicaid or to limit the program to certain groups of people, such as the elderly or the disabled.

States that do not offer medically needy programs have a strict income cap and do not allow individuals to spend down to the allowable income level. Applicants in some states may still qualify for Medicaid, however, by setting up a Miller Trust, also known as a Qualified Income Trust. Redirecting all or just the excess income into a special purpose trust has the same effect as lowering income because the state does not count this income when determining Medicaid eligibility. Income from the trust could then be used to pay an elderly person's share of cost.

The rules for spending down income or setting up and administering a Miller Trust are complex and very specific to each state. I recommend that you find a qualified elder law attorney to guide you. You can find attorneys through your state bar association, local voluntary bar associations, and local legal referral services.

What happens when a Medicaid recipient dies and still has money left over?

Under the Medicaid Estate Recovery Program (MERP), the federal government requires states to recoup money spent on the deceased's behalf for long-term care. Only Medicaid recipients who were fifty-five years of age or older when they received benefits or recipients of any age who were institutionalized, are affected. States must provide estate recovery waivers for undue hardship cases and may forego recovery for other reasons, such as the cost of selling the deceased's property exceeds its worth, or the amount to be recovered is relatively small.

Will Medicaid pay a family member to provide personal care services for my relative?

Under some state consumer-directed programs, Medicaid recipients may select their own paid caregiver, including a family member. The Medicaid recipient, as employer, is responsible for payroll, taxes, insurance, and workers' compensation, but is permitted to outsource the paperwork.

Can people receive Medicare and Medicaid at the same time?

Participation in Medicare does not preclude participation in Medicaid. Individuals who qualify for both programs simultaneously are called "dual eligible" beneficiaries.

Does Social Security pay for long-term care in the home?

Social Security is a federal program funded by payroll taxes to benefit workers who paid into the system. The program does not offer a specific benefit for long-term care, but the government pays recipients directly each month and individuals are free to use their money as they wish, including for this purpose.

People may begin collecting reduced Social Security benefits at age sixty-two and full benefits between the ages of sixty-six and sixty-seven. Payments increase the longer individuals wait to begin receiving payments until they reach seventy, after which the amount remains flat, except for cost-of-living increases that affect all beneficiaries.

Are there Social Security benefits for spouses?

A wife, for example, sixty-two years of age or older, may qualify for Social Security benefits based on her husband's earnings record. The wife may be able to collect benefits before the age of sixty-two if she cares for a child younger than sixteen or a child with a qualifying disability. The husband must have already filed to collect benefits and the couple must have been married for at least one year. It does not matter if the wife ever worked.

Even an ex-wife sixty-two years of age or older may qualify for benefits if the marriage lasted ten years or longer and the ex-wife is still single. Whether the husband must already be receiving benefits depends on several factors. Contact the Social Security Administration for more information.

Do survivors' benefits cover in-home long-term care?

Survivors' benefits are part of the Social Security program that pays some or all of a deceased person's benefits to the surviving spouse or dependent children. These payments can be used for anything, including long-term care expenses. Surviving spouses may collect reduced benefits at sixty years of age and full benefits between the ages of sixty-six and sixty-seven. Disabled spouses may begin collecting benefits at the age of fifty. Surviving spouses who receive their own Social Security benefits are entitled to the deceased's benefits if higher than their own, but not both. Divorced individuals remain eligible for their deceased ex-spouse's Social Security benefits even if the decedent remarried, provided the claimant was married to the deceased ex-spouse for at least ten years and did not remarry before age sixty, or age fifty if disabled.

Does Supplemental Security Income (SSI) pay for long-term care in the home?

SSI is a federal program that provides benefits to disabled individuals with limited income. There is no separate long-term care component, but SSI recipients receive a monthly check that can be applied to anything, including the cost of in-home care. The goal of the program is to raise recipients' income to an amount pre-set by the government each year. An individual must be at least sixty-five years old to collect SSI unless the Social Security Administration declares the person blind or disabled. Then, the person may begin receiving payments as early as eighteen years old. Some people are eligible for both Social Security and SSI, and most states supplement the federal government's SSI payments.

Financial eligibility requirements are determined by the state. If your relative is contemplating a move to another state, investigate that state's requirements to avoid unpleasant surprises.

How does Social Security Disability Insurance (SSDI) differ?

The primary difference between SSDI and SSI is that SSDI recipients must have worked a certain number of years and paid payroll taxes during that period. If they become disabled after earning enough quarters, they may qualify for SSDI benefits, which can be used for anything, including long-term care expenses.

Does health insurance pay for long-term care?

Traditional private health insurance policies almost never pay for custodial or long-term care. Many plans cover hospice care in the home if the insured person meets life expectancy and other requirements.

What is long-term care insurance and does it pay for in-home care?

Insurance companies have created specific products to help people pay for long-term care if they become ill or disabled. Some policies pay for in-home care while others only cover skilled care in a nursing home. Under a typical plan, a policyholder elects to receive a predetermined amount of money for a specified period such as thirty-five hundred dollars per month for five years, or in the case of many earlier policies, as long as the policyholder requires long-term care. Like other forms of insurance, the cost depends on many factors, such as the policyholder's age, health, type of plan selected, the state in which the person lives, and if the policy includes inflation protection to keep up with the rising cost of health care. Long-term care insurers have the right to deny coverage for pre-existing conditions.

Some plans give the policyholder a set amount to use as the person sees fit, while other plans require the policyholder to submit receipts for reimbursement. Private caregivers rarely accept insurance as a form of payment, whereas most agencies do.

Despite the likely need for long-term care, the American Association for Long-Term Care Insurance estimates that only about ten million people have purchased this type of coverage.[xxxv] Premiums are expensive and many existing policyholders have seen steep increases over the years. Most insurance companies got out of the long-term care insurance market altogether after claims exceeded projections, fewer people than anticipated allowed their policy to lapse, and projected earnings on invested premiums fell short of forecasts.

Will long-term care insurance pay a family member to provide personal care services?

It depends on the policy. Some plans will, while others will not pay for a family member who resides in the same household. It is easier to get a plan to pay a family member if a formal contract is in place between the senior and the person providing care. Also, some policies require family members to obtain training before they can receive pay.

When does my long-term care policy go into effect?

People cannot just tap into their long-term care coverage because they want or even need assistance. Usually, policyholders must be unable to perform a stated number of ADLs (two is the norm) or have a cognitive impairment such as dementia or a brain injury. Some plans require hospitalization before benefits can start. If your relative only needs assistance with ADLs, the prerequisite of a hospital stay could be problematic.

Also, long-term care insurance policies usually include an "elimination period," or a certain number of days that must pass before coverage begins. During that time, policyholders are responsible for their own long-term care expenses.

Can my relative's life insurance policy be used to pay for long-term care?

It depends on the type of policy that your loved one has. Certain types of life insurance, such as whole, universal, and variable life, include a savings component, which accumulates over time. As the policy matures, policyholders can take out a loan against the cash value that has built up. Alternatively, policyholders can surrender their policy altogether to the insurance company and withdraw the cash surrender value that has built up. This amount will be less than the full death benefit. Term life insurance does not accumulate any cash value.

Also, check to see if your relative's policy permits cash advances against the death benefit amount. An accelerated death benefit, for example, allows policyholders who become chronically, critically, or terminally ill to withdraw a portion of the death benefit with the remainder going to their beneficiaries. In some cases, only certain illnesses and diseases are covered or policyholders must be unable to perform a specified number of ADLs.

Your parent's life insurance policy may include a long-term care rider. These plans provide a monthly payment to use toward expenses. The beneficiaries will receive a tax-free death benefit if some or none of the long-term care benefits are used.

A policyholder with a terminal illness and a life expectancy of only a few years may also be able to sell their life insurance policy to a third party for a lump sum. Under this arrangement, called a viatical settlement, the purchaser pays more than the cash surrender value but less than the death benefit amount. The third party takes over payment of the premiums and receives the full death benefit amount upon the policyholder's death. These transactions are usually handled by viatical settlement companies, which are licensed by most states. The purchaser may require proof of the terminal illness plus a certification from a physician that the policyholder's life expectancy falls within the company's acceptable range.

Another product to help seniors fund their long-term care expenses is the life settlement. Individuals sell their life insurance policy to a third party for an amount that is higher than the policy's cash surrender value, but less than the death benefit. Policyholders are usually at least sixty-five years old with a serious health issue but, unlike in the case of viatical settlements, do not have to have a terminal illness. The purchaser assumes responsibility for the premiums.

Long-term care annuities—where the insurance company sends policyholders a monthly income stream over a predetermined period or for life—are another option. If needed, the policyholder can access the accumulated funds to pay for assistance. With some plans, the long-term care benefit doubles. Upon death, any remaining value in the policy will go to the named beneficiaries.

In some instances, taking cash out of a life insurance policy can affect your parent's Medicaid eligibility. Therefore, it is important to find out if this is the case before moving forward.

What is a reverse mortgage and can it be used to pay for long-term care?

A person's home is usually their most valuable asset. A federally insured reverse mortgage is a type of loan that allows homeowners sixty-two years of age or older to borrow a portion of the equity from their principal residence. The loan amount is based on the borrower's age, the amount of equity in the home, and the interest rate. There are no restrictions on how the money can be used. The borrower elects to receive the money in one of three ways: a lump sum payment, regular fixed monthly payments, or a line of credit. People with reverse mortgages retain title and ownership of their home and are still responsible for property taxes, insurance, and upkeep of the property.

When is the loan repaid on a reverse mortgage?

The loan from a reverse mortgage becomes due when the last surviving borrower

- dies
- sells the home

- conveys the title to someone else
- moves out of the home for a period exceeding twelve consecutive months, including moving into a nursing home or assisted living facility
- fails to pay property taxes, homeowners' insurance, or condominium fees, resulting in a lien on the property
- allows the home to fall into disrepair

If the heirs want to keep the home, they have to repay the loan. If the home is sold, the heirs get any proceeds left after the loan is repaid. Reverse mortgages have high fees and people need to understand exactly what is involved with this type of loan. Interest on the loan accumulates until the loan is repaid. To protect consumers, the federal government requires prospective borrowers to get counseling from a HUD-approved counseling agency before applying for a reverse mortgage.

Will a reverse mortgage affect any government benefits I receive?

People receiving need-based public benefits such as Medicaid and SSI could jeopardize their eligibility if the proceeds from a reverse mortgage put them over the asset limit. With knowledge and careful planning, however, borrowers can avoid this situation. Reverse mortgages do not affect government entitlements such as Social Security or Medicare.

Does the U.S. Department of Veterans Affairs (VA) provide long-term care benefits to veterans?

The VA's Aid and Attendance (A&A) and Housebound programs provide tax-free monthly financial assistance to help qualified veterans or their surviving spouse with the cost of in-home long-term care. The eligibility rules are very specific and mistakes on the initial application can delay benefits. Consider contacting a non-profit advocacy organization for veterans or a VA-accredited law firm for assistance.

Are there VA benefits to help family caregivers of veterans?

Both the Housebound and the Aid and Attendance benefits allow veterans to pay family members to provide caregiver services but the Housebound Program excludes spouses. The VA also administers the Program of Comprehensive Assistance for Family Caregivers, which provides a monthly stipend to primary caregivers of qualifying veterans. Currently, this program only covers veterans who have at least a 70% service-connected disability rating from the VA resulting from a serious illness or injury sustained in the line of duty on or before May 7, 1975 or on or after September 11, 2001. The VA hopes to expand the program to include veterans from other periods. For a complete list of eligibility requirements, visit the VA's website (see Resources).

Are there special long-term care programs for tribal communities?

Yes, several tribal communities have programs that provide in-home assistance—White Earth in Minnesota, the Pueblo of Zuni in New Mexico, the Oneida in Wisconsin, and the Cherokee in Oklahoma, to name a few. Most programs serve the elderly, but others cover disabled and developmentally-delayed individuals as well. Consult the website for the Centers for Medicare and Medicaid Services (see Resources).

CHAPTER 8

THE FUTURE OF LONG-TERM CARE

The graying of America is upon us. Since January 1, 2011, more than ten thousand baby boomers have turned sixty-five every day and this trend will continue until 2030.[xxxvi] The federal government estimates that more than seventy percent of people sixty-five years of age or older will need some type of long-term care during their lifetime due to physical limitations, illness, or cognitive impairment.[xxxvii] Today, over six million Americans are living with Alzheimer's, the most common form of dementia.[xxxviii]

The quality of life of millions of old, frail, and disabled Americans hangs in the balance as this country grapples with the need for affordable long-term in-home care. There was a time when seniors could count on younger family members to care for them in their old age, but eldercare as we knew it no longer exists. Most baby boomers, the largest generation ever to retire, have expressed a desire to remain in their home, if possible. This chapter looks at the challenges facing seniors who want to age in place and examines trends in the public and private sectors that will affect the delivery of services in the decades ahead.

The greatest obstacle facing individuals who need in-home care is the shortage of professional caregivers. At a time when the demand for home care for seniors and disabled individuals is exploding, the available labor pool is dwindling. Professional caregivers are leaving the field at an alarming rate, making retention of workers extremely difficult. Low pay, few benefits, high stress, physically arduous work, long hours, concern about exposure to highly contagious diseases, limited opportunities for advancement, injuries, and violence in the workplace are all contributing factors. According to a 2019 report, the turnover rate for home care aides was sixty-four percent.[xxxix]

Experts and scholars working in the home care field predict that America will have to rely on immigrant labor to meet the unprecedented need for caregivers. American workers alone cannot solve the shortage because the demand is simply too great. A study published by the Paraprofessional Healthcare Institute (PHI) in 2021 reported that people of color comprise about sixty-three percent of caregivers working in a home setting.[xl] As the CEO of a nursing home remarked, "[w]hat people don't seem to understand is that people from other countries really are the backbone of long-term care."[xli]

Immigrant direct care workers are more prevalent in some states than others. In 2018, more than fifty percent of home health aides in New York, New Jersey, and Florida were immigrants.[xlii]

The main threats to foreign labor in the United States are restrictive immigration policies, which will only ensure that the caregiver shortage continues. A failure to comprehend that immigrant caregivers take jobs that Americans do not want because of low pay and lack of upward mobility—among other issues—reduces the likelihood the problem will be corrected. Other countries with large aging populations, such as Canada and Japan, are experiencing caregiver shortages, too, but they are handling the problem differently. In 2019, Canada initiated a new pilot program specifically designed to attract immigrant caregivers. Unlike their previous program, workers can now bring family members with them if they can support their relatives. In addition, caregivers are no longer required to live with the family employing them and, after working for two years, workers can apply for permanent residency.

Japan is also reaching out to foreign-born caregivers, primarily from other Asian countries. Japan saw a marked increase in the number of foreigners entering to work as caregivers after the country changed its immigration laws specifically to address the shortage. Now, foreigners can attain resident status in Japan once they complete their training from an accredited school and the state certifies them as caregivers. Prior to the change in law, applicants needed three years of work experience in the field and had to pass a national exam in the fourth year. Foreign caregivers still face racism, and the language barrier has proved to be a steep hurdle for most applicants, but at least the government has acknowledged these issues and is trying to address them.

In contrast, there is no direct pathway to resident status or citizenship for foreigners who want to work as caregivers in the United States. The possibility of American citizenship has always been an attractive draw for foreigners. Our government must get realistic about this country's dependence on foreign labor for certain occupations, such as caregivers, or America may find itself without a chair when the music stops. Given the stark statistics about the caregiver shortage, foreign workers are a viable option that should be vigorously pursued, not blocked. As the United States tightens its immigration policies and contemplates more stringent citizenship requirements, this country may lose any competitive edge that it had in attracting immigrant labor.

It has also been suggested that workers who lose their job to automation might be candidates for caregiver positions. A recent article about the impact of robots states that twenty million manufacturing jobs could disappear because of automation.[xliii] For these displaced workers to become interested in the caregiving field, the position would need to become more professional. Currently, many states and agencies prohibit caregivers from performing tasks usually performed by licensed direct care workers with medical training, such as nurses. However, someone other than a nurse can handle many of these responsibilities just as well. Giving caregivers more responsibility will raise their pay and attract many individuals who have lost their job to technology.

Another challenge facing those who need long-term care is the high cost of paid caregivers. The cost of long-term care has increased astronomically over the last decade with no sign of leveling off. Companies will continue to launch new financial products aimed at helping people meet this cost.

There have been several proposals calling for the federal

government to establish a program similar to Medicare that helps pay for long-term care. So far, however, these ideas have failed to gain any traction. The IRS does allow taxpayers to deduct a portion of their long-term care insurance premiums. The amount varies depending on the taxpayer's age, with older individuals being able to deduct more than younger people. Also, Senator Patrick Toomey of Pennsylvania re-introduced a bill in 2021—the Long-Term Care Affordability Act—that would allow individuals to withdraw up to two thousand five hundred dollars per year from their retirement accounts tax free to pay for long-term care insurance. Most experts do not believe that the federal government will ever do more than use the tax code to incentivize individuals to shoulder the cost of long-term care on their own.

In contrast to the federal government, Washington became the first state in the nation to enact a state-operated long-term care benefits program. Funded by a payroll tax on Washington employees—with some exceptions—eligible workers can receive up to a hundred dollars a day for a lifetime benefit of thirty-six thousand, five hundred dollars beginning in 2025. The money can be used for a range of services including at-home personal care. Employees must be unable to perform at least three ADLs to receive benefits. Qualified workers who had a comparable long-term care insurance policy before November 1, 2021, can apply for an exemption from paying the tax. Other states are closely watching and may adopt programs of their own in the future.

Some seniors are tackling the cost issue by trying to save in other areas such as housing. Over the years, I have heard numerous women say that when they get older, they want to live just like the Golden Girls, the hit TV show. The owner rented out rooms in her home for additional income and the weekly episodes were about four women, including a mother/daughter duo, living together and supporting one another. Taking on one or more roommates is not unusual for the young and single, especially in high rent markets. But older people are not used to living with strangers. Given the shortage of family caregivers and the high cost of caregiving, however, more older adults who want companionship, help with daily household chores, or extra income are open to the idea of sharing their home. Sites such as Silvernest and Senior Homeshares have sprung up to fill this market (see Resources). These companies allow older homeowners to list their residences to attract compatible roommates. The services vary for each company. Some sites will match subscribers with compatible roommates and perform background checks for a fee.

Technology will continue to change the caregiving industry just as it impacts every other field. Many companies are investing in robotics to solve the caregiver shortage and other issues affecting eldercare. The obvious benefit of robots is that machines are available to assist their owners around the clock. They also will not call in sick or suddenly quit. Robots can help seniors feel more self-sufficient. Instead of depending on others for simple tasks, such as retrieving an item from another room, seniors can merely summon their robot. Of course, there are numerous jobs that only a human can do and innumerable ways in which humans interact with each other for which robots are no substitute—at least not yet.

The International Federation of Robotics projects that sales of robots designed to help seniors will increase. Machines that transfer people from beds to chairs and dispense pills are in the experimental stages and are currently being tested in nursing homes. Today's robots can sense extreme temperatures, such as a fire, or detect items in a senior's path that could cause the person to fall. Some robots can navigate stairs and use sign language. Panasonic's robotics division has introduced a hospital bed that converts to a motorized wheelchair. In the area of household tasks, machines such as the Roomba from the iRobot company, vacuums, sweeps, and mops floors. The day when robots prepare meals, do laundry, and help seniors dress and bathe may not be too far off.

Companionship is another need that some inventors believe robots can fulfill for the elderly. Robots designed to alleviate loneliness are being manufactured in the form of plush cuddly animals such as rabbits, baby seals, and bears. Some of these machines are voice-activated and have the ability to play games and, thereby, provide mental stimulation, play music, issue medication reminders, and encourage elders to take a walk or drink some water. In an effort to make companion robots seem more humanlike, inventors are building machines with the ability to make eye contact, make soft reassuring sounds, and even read facial expressions. The latter ability would be helpful in detecting if a senior is in distress.

Artificial intelligence may be the very advancement that causes seniors to finally embrace technology, but not everyone is on board with the idea of using robots to provide companionship. Physical touch is important to good health, whereas the lack of a human touch can lead to depression. As one gerontologist put it, "Humans need humans."[xliv] Whether robots are an adequate substitute for a human is anybody's guess. But supporters point out that companionship from a robot is better than no companionship at all, and given the shortage of caregivers, that's the choice some seniors will face.

Animated virtual pets or avatars represent another technology being tried out on seniors. Cute animals pop up on the computer to help ease seniors' feelings of isolation and depression by providing emotional support and reminding them to take their medication, eat well, and exercise. On-screen avatars by the Gerijoy company are controlled around the clock by humans who converse with elders using special technology.

The ultimate goal of developers of robots and avatars is to have them act and react as much like humans as possible. Element Care, a PACE organization, has deployed avatars into the homes of some of its clients with positive results and expects to expand the program.

Concierge services targeting the well-to-do elderly is another trend that is growing. Seniors with financial means can continue to enjoy pursuits and conveniences that only money can buy. Imagine hiring a caregiver to accompany your loved one on their ten-day cruise around the Greek islands or spend the winter in Florida with them. Your parent's regular caregiver may have obligations preventing them from going on such trips, but senior concierge services now provide caregivers who are available for travel of any duration.

As you can see, the future of long-term care is all over the map at this point. To stay informed, it is imperative that you check the literature from time to time for developments in the field of long-term in-home care.

RESOURCES

AARP
(888) 687-2277
www.aarp.org

Administration for Community Living
(202) 401-4634
www.acl.gov

Aging Care
www.agingcare.com

Aging Life Care Association
(520) 881-8008
www.aginglifecare.org

Alliance for Home Health Quality and Innovation
950 F Street, NW
Washington, DC 20001
(202) 239-3427
www.ahhqi.org

alzheimers.net
www.alzheimers.net

American Association of Daily Money Managers
174 Crestview Drive
Bellefonte, PA 16823-8516
(814) 357-9191
www.aadmm.com

American Association for Long-term Care Insurance
(818) 597-3227
www.aaltci.org

American Council on Aging
www.medicaidplanningassistance.org

Care.com
www.care.com

Centers for Disease Control and Prevention
(800) 232-4636
www.cdc.gov

Centers for Medicare and Medicaid Services
www.cms.gov

Data and Marketing Association
www.DMAChoice.org

Dementia Society of America
(800) 336-3684
www.dementiasociety.org

Direct Mail Association
www.dmachoice.org

Elder Fraud Hotline
U.S. Department of Justice
(833) 372-8311

Eldercare Locator
(800) 677-1116
www.eldercare.acl.gov

Equifax
www.equifax.com

Experian
www.experian.com

Family Caregiver Alliance
235 Montgomery Street, Suite 930

San Francisco, CA. 94104
(800) 445-8106
www.caregiver.org

Federal Trade Commission
www.ftc.gov

Genworth
www.genworth.com

GoGoGrandparent
(855) 464-6872
www.GoGoGrandparent.com

Grandpad
www.GrandPad.net

Handbook for Long-Distance Caregivers
Publication Orders
Family Caregiver Alliance
235 Montgomery Street, Suite 930
San Francisco, CA 94104

Internal Revenue Service
www.irs.gov

International Federation of Robotics
www.ifr.org

Lotsa Helping Hands
www.lotsahelpinghands.com

National Adult Protective Services Association
www.napsa-now.org

National Association of Area Agencies on Aging
1100 New Jersey Avenue, SE, Suite 350

Washington, DC 20003
(202) 872-0888
www.n4a.org

National Association for Home Care & Hospice
228 7th Street, SE
Washington, DC 20003
www.nahc.org

National Center on Elder Abuse
(855) 500-3537
https://ncea.acl.gov

National Council on Aging
www.ncoa.org

National Employment Law Project
www.nelp.org

National Institute on Aging
31 Center Drive, MSC 2292
Bethesda, MD 20892
(800) 222-2225
www.nia.nih.gov

National PACE Association
www.npaonline.org

National Sex Offender Registry
www.nsopw.gov

OptOutPrescreen
www.optoutprescreen.com

Paraprofessional Healthcare Institute
400 East Fordham Rd., 11th Floor
Bronx, NY 10458

(718) 402-7766
www.phinational.org

Paying for Senior Care
www.payingforseniorcare.com

Senior Homeshares
2890 Shadow Creek Drive
Suite 305
Boulder, CO 80303
www.seniorhomeshares.com

Silvernest
www.silvernest.com

Tech Enhanced Life
www.techenhancedlife.com

Transunion
www.transunion.com

U.S. Bureau of Labor Statistics
www.bls.gov

U.S. Citizenship and Immigration Services
www.uscis.gov

U.S. Department of Homeland Security
www.dhs.gov

U.S. Department of Justice
www.justice.gov

U.S. Department of Labor
www.dol.gov

U.S. Department of Veterans Affairs
(877) 222-VETS
www.va.gov

U.S. Postal Service
www.usps.com

U.S. Social Security Administration
www.ssa.gov

Village to Village Network
www.vtvnetwork.org

Visual Senior
www.visualsenior.com

INDEX

NOTES

[i] "Prevent Falls and Fractures," National Institute on Aging, accessed April 5, 2022, https://www.nia.nih.gov/health/prevent-falls-and-fractures.

[ii] Carol Marak. 2016, "Elder Orphans: A Baby Boomer's Aging-Alone Plan," *HuffPost*, January 4, 2016, https://www.huffpost.com/entry/aging-alone-plan_b_8886418.

[iii] "Occupational Employment and Wage Statistics," Bureau of Labor Statistics, accessed May 15, 2022, https://www.bls.gov/oes/current/oes311120.htm.

[iv] National Institute on Aging. 2018. "Geriatric care managers can make daily life easier for caregivers." *San Diego Union-Tribune*, April 24, 2018.

[v] Egan, Paul. 2015. "Judge tosses family's lawsuit in elder caregiver case." *Detroit Free Press*, October 1, 2015.

[vi] "Live-in Domestic Service Workers Under the Labor Standards Act (FLSA)," Department of Labor, 2021, accessed September 30, 2021, https://www.dol.gov/agencies/whd/fact-sheets/79b-flsa-live-in-domestic-workers.

[vii] "Faulty FBI Background Checks for Employment: Correcting FBI Records is Key to Criminal Justice Reform," National Employment Law Project, accessed July 13, 2020, https://www.nelp.org/publication/faulty-fbi-background-checks-for-employment/.

[viii] *Caregiver Roulette: California Fails to Screen those who Care for the Elderly at Home, Before the California Senate Office of Oversight and Outcomes* (2011) (statement of John Hill, Principal Consultant). https://sooo.senate.ca.gov/sites/sooo.senate.ca.gov/files/2385.caregiver%20roulette.pdf.

[ix] "Adult Protective Services Abuse Registry National Report," National Adult Protective Services Association, March 2018, Adult Protective Services Abuse Registry National Report," https://www.napsa-now.org/napsa-aps-abuse-registry-project/.

[x] Maura Dolan. 2014. "Court says paid caregivers can't sue if injured by Alzheimer patients," *Los Angeles Times*, August 4, 2014, https://www.latimes.com/local/la-me-alzheimers-lawsuits-20140805-story.html.

[xi] Span, Paula. 2018. "In Elderly Hands, Firearms Can Be Even Deadlier." *The New York Times*, May 25, 2018.

[xii] Ibid.

[xiii] "Hours Worked Applicable to Domestic Service Employment Under the Fair Labor Standards Act (FLSA)," Department of Labor, accessed January 4, 2021, https://www.dol.gov/agencies/whd/field-assistance-bulletins/2016-1.

[xiv] Leland, John. 2008. "In 'Sweetie' and 'Dear,' a Hurt for the Elderly." *The New York Times*, October 6, 2008.

[xv] "Breaks and Meal Periods," Department of Labor, 2021, accessed March 10, 2021, https://www.dol.gov/general/topic/workhours/breaks.

[xvi] Heath, Thomas. 2018. "Your home health care aide is not your maid, landscaper or party organizer." *The Washington Post*, July 13, 2018.

[xvii] Londberg, Max. 2017. "Smithville woman charged with stealing hospice patient's pain medication." *The Kansas City Star*, March 15, 2017.

[xviii] Vielmeteti, Bruce and Mary Spicuzza. 2017. "Couple charged with scamming home, cash from 92-year-old neighbor with dementia." *Milwaukee Journal Sentinel*, December 5, 2017.

[xix] National Floor Safety Institute, https://www.nfsi.org/nfsi-research/quick-facts. Accessed January 3, 2022.

[xx] Morse, Dan. 2015. "Elderly Bethesda man bilked of hundreds of thousands of dollars." *The Washington Post*, October 15, 2015.

[xxi] "Elder Abuse Statistics," Department of Justice, accessed September 10, 2021, https://www.justice.gov/file/1098056/download.

[xxii] "Elder Abuse Statistics," Department of Justice, accessed September 10, 2021, https://www.justice.gov/file/1098056/download.

[xxiii] Winegar, Jed. August 18, 2016. "Perpetrators of Elder Abuse Are Usually Family Members," National Care Planning Council, https://www.longtermcarelink.net/article-2016-8-18-Perpetrators-of-Elder-Abuse-Are-Usually-Family-Members.htm.

[xxiv] "Violence Prevention," Centers for Disease Control and Prevention, accessed June 13, 2020, https://www.cdc.gov/violenceprevention/elderabuse/fastfact.html.

[xxv] "What is Elder Abuse," Administration for Community Living, accessed September 5, 2021, https://acl.gov/programs/elder-justice/what-elder-abuse.

[xxvi] "Violence Prevention," Centers for Disease Control and Prevention, accessed June 13, 2020, https://www.cdc.gov/violenceprevention/elderabuse/fastfact.html.

[xxvii] "Research, Statistics and Data," National Center on Elder Abuse, accessed February 28, 2021, https://ncea.acl.gov/What-We-Do/Research/Statistics-and-Data.aspx#types.

[xxviii] "Violence Prevention," Centers for Disease Control and Prevention, accessed June 13, 2020, https://www.cdc.gov/violenceprevention/elderabuse/fastfact.html.

[xxix] Department of Justice, The United States Attorney's Office, Eastern District of Virginia, "Caregiver Sentenced to Prison for Defrauding Client of $100K," news release, Friday, April 26, 2019, https://www.justice.gov/usao-edva/pr/caregiver-sentenced-prison-defrauding-client-100k.

[xxx] "14 Red Flags for Elder Financial Abuse," American Bankers Association, July 17, 2017, https://www.aba.com/news-research/research-analysis/14-red-flags-for-elder-financial-abuse#.

[xxxi] "Research, Statistics and Data," National Center on Elder Abuse, accessed February 28, 2021, https://ncea.acl.gov/What-We-Do/Research/Statistics-and-Data.aspx#types.

[xxxii] "New Study Finds Many Agencies Place Unqualified Caregivers in Homes of the Elderly," Northwestern Medicine, July 10, 2012, https://news.feinberg.northwestern.edu/2012/07/dangerous_caregivers/.

[xxxiii] "Cost of Care Survey," www.genworth.com/aging-and-you/finances/cost-of-care.html, accessed May 10, 2022.

[xxxiv] Redfoot, Donald, Lynn Feinberg, and Ari Houser. "The Aging of the Baby Boomers and the Growing Care Gap: A Look at the Future Availability of Family Caregivers," Public Policy Institute, August 2013, https://www.aarp.org/home-family/caregiving/info-08-2013/the-aging-of-the-baby-boom-and-the-growing-care-gap-AARP-ppi-ltc.html.

[xxxv] American Association for Long-term Care Insurance, https://www.aaltci.org. Accessed January 12, 2022.

[xxxvi] "2020 Census Will Help Policymakers Prepare for the Incoming Wave of Aging Boomers," U.S. Census Bureau, December 10, 2019, https://www.census.gov/library/stories/2019/12/by-2030-all-baby-boomers-will-be-age-65-or-older.html.

[xxxvii] "Caregiver Resources & Long-Term Care," U.S. Department of Health and Human Services, accessed September 22, 2021, https://www.hhs.gov/aging/long-term-care/index.html.

[xxxviii] "2019 Alzheimer's Statistics." https://www.alzheimers.net. Accessed January 13, 2022.

[xxxix] Holly, Robert. 2020. "Caregiver Turnover Rate Falls to 64% as Home Care Agencies 'Flatten the Curve'," June 17, 2020, https://homehealthcarenews.com/2020/06/caregiver-turnover-rate-falls-to-64-as-home-care-agencies-flatten-the-curve.

[xl] Espinoza, Robert. "Direct Care Workers in the United States: Key Facts," Paraprofessional Healthcare Institute, September 8, 2020, https://phinational.org/resource/direct-care-workers-in-the-united-states-key-facts-2/.

[xli] Bailey, Melissa. 2018. "As Trump targets immigrants, elderly brace to lose caregivers." *Los Angeles Times*, March 27, 2018.

[xlii] Batalova, Jeanne. "Immigrant Health-Care Workers in the United States," Migration Policy Institute, May 14, 2020, https://www.migrationpolicy.org/article/immigrant-health-care-workers-united-states-2018.

[xliii] Catherine Bosley. "Robots May Displace 20 Million Manufacturing Jobs by 2030," *Bloomberg*, June 25, 2019, https://www.bloombergquint.com/business/robots-rise-may-displace-20-million-manufacturing-jobs-by-2030.

[xliv] Bursack, Carol B. "Do Robots Have a Place in Elder Care," agingcare.com, https://www.agingcare.com/Articles/robots-in-elder-care-170581.htm (Accessed October 16, 2020.

MEET THE AUTHOR

The idea for *Finding the Right Caregiver, Getting the Best Care* grew out of the author's experience managing her mother's long-term care for several years. In addition, the author holds an interdisciplinary Certificate on Aging from Johns Hopkins University, a master's degree in Adult Education, and a law degree. She has also worked as a certified volunteer long-term care ombudsman in her home state.

Made in the USA
Las Vegas, NV
16 April 2024

88760398R00115